THE COMING OF THE

GOLDEN AGE

A VIEW OF THE END OF PROGRESS

BY GUNTHER S. STENT

Published for
The American Museum of Natural History
The Natural History Press
Garden City, New York

The line illustrations for this book which appear
on pages 8, 37, 39, 40, 63 and 94
were prepared by the Graphic Arts Division of
The American Museum of Natural History.

TO INGA LOFTSDOTTIR

ACKNOWLEDGMENTS

Despite his disagreement with its main conclusions, this book owes much to Niels Jerne. Seemingly interminable arguments with him in the past few years allowed me to organize my thoughts about the Golden Age. He first encouraged me to put these notions in writing, steered me to some of the relevant literature, and provided me with incisive comments of successive versions of the manuscript. I also thank Jack Dunitz and Ronald Stent for their vigorous and helpful criticisms. I am indebted to Benoit Mandelbrot for revising that part of my manuscript which deals with second-stage indeterminism and for having thus minimized the risk of my misrepresenting his views. I acknowledge my gratitude to Margery Hoogs, who, as she has done repeatedly for the past twelve years, once more trained her perceptive critique of style on my writing.

In 1967, I was able to present a preliminary, two-lecture statement of the ideas covered in this book at the Collège de France and at Kansas State University, thanks to invitations arranged by Francois Jacob and Karl G. Lark. The first of these two lectures has now been published under the title "That Was the Molecular Biology That Was" in *Science*, Vol. 160, pp. 390–95 (1968). The present, expanded version represents the text of seven public lectures which I delivered at the University of California, Berkeley, in 1968, during my temporary appointment as Professor of Arts and Sciences. I am indebted to the Berkeley Chancellor and Board of Educational Development for having provided me with the freedom from my regular academic duties necessary for writing this book.

CONTENTS

IT IS ALMOST THE YEAR
TWO THOUSAND

To start the world of old
We had one age of gold
Not labored out of mines,
And some say there are signs,
The second such has come,
The true Millennium,
The final golden glow
To end it. And if so
(and science ought to know)
We may well raise our heads
From weeding garden beds
And annotating books
To watch this end de luxe.

ROBERT FROST

PROLOGUE

The trauma inflicted on the University of California professors by the 1964 Free Speech Movement of the Berkeley students forced upon me and many of my colleagues an agonizing reappraisal of earlier and now obviously outdated attitudes regarding our life's work. At the outset, the prevalent faculty view of the Movement had been that it was just one more tempest in a teapot. But by the time its revolutionary drama—with our then Chancellor in the role of Louis XVI, our Academic Senate as the Estates-General, our Administration Building as the Bastille, and our charismatic student leader Mario Savio as Danton—had run its course, most of us had finally appreciated the cosmic significance of those events. For it appeared to us that Berkeley had become the stage on which the global future of higher education was being acted out. Friends beyond Berkeley to whom I then communicated these insights generally dismissed them as a form of parochial paranoia, but I think that later, more or less parallel, developments at universities around the world were soon to confirm the justice of our earlier apocalyptic vision. In my subsequent efforts to understand the deeper causes underlying the Free Speech Movement, I came to believe that its manifestations were merely symptoms of the new epoch of history, the Golden Age, which mankind is about to enter.

There could be few thoughts less original and more trite nowadays than the idea that a new age is dawning; everyone seems to have noticed it. Indeed, the writing of essays signaling the advent of a new age—mankind at the crossroads of its evolution, the end of history—has now reached epidemic proportions. And so I make no claims to originality when I consecrate my essay to the Golden Age whose onset *I* happen to envisage. With the coming of this Golden Age, the arts and sciences will have reached the end of their long road. The Golden Age to which I refer is that of Greek mythology, recorded by Hesiod in the eighth century B.C. According to this myth, the present obviously miserable Iron Age is but the fifth stage in a constantly deteriorating series of stages, the first stage of which was the Golden Age. In that Golden Age, a golden race of mortal men dwelt on Earth, who "lived like gods without sorrow of heart, remote and free from toil and grief, miserable age rested not on them, but with legs and arms never failing they made merry feasting beyond the reach of all evil. When they died, it was as though they were overcome with sleep, and they had all good things; for the fruitful earth bore them fruit abundantly without stint. They dwelt in ease and peace upon their lands with many good things, rich in flocks and loved by the blessed gods." This Golden Age, according to Hesiod, presently came to an end when Pandora lifted the lid of her box and allowed the escape and spread of previously unknown evils. The Golden Age was then succeeded by the Silver, Brass, and Heroic Ages, each age worse than its predecessor, and finally by our own Iron Age. In our own Iron Age men "never rest from labor and sorrow by day, and from perishing by night; and the gods shall lay sore trouble upon them."

The purpose of this essay is the attempt to show that the ancients' view of human history was topsy-turvy, in that the Golden Age is not the very first but the very last stage of history, and one that is a necessary successor, rather than an antecedent, of the Iron Age. I shall try to show that unmistakable signs of the advent of the Golden Age, and all that it portends, are already with us, at least in the industrially advanced nations. I doubt, however, that Hesiod, or any other of the legion of writers who pined for lost paradises since his time, would find this Golden Age very much to his liking. This realization that the Golden Age is, in fact, lugubrious is also by no means new; it is implicit in the writings of Ortega y Gasset and was most forcefully developed by Aldous Huxley in his *Brave New World*.

My general argument will follow more or less Hegelian (or, for all I know, Marxist) lines. I shall try to show that internal contradictions—theses and antitheses—in progress, art, science, and other phenomena relevant to the human condition make these processes self-limiting; that these processes are reaching their limits in our time and that they all lead to one final, grand synthesis, the Golden Age. To make this argument, I will have to range over a vast spectrum of human activity and touch upon many subjects: philosophy, psychology, economics, history, painting, music, and physics, for which I have no professional qualifications. Hence, so that my readers will not find themselves confronted with a work representing nothing but the rantings of a rank dilettante, I have devoted the first four chapters to the field in which I *am* a professional, namely molecular genetics. More precisely, I will describe the history of my field in order to show that its rise and fall is but a paradigm of the history of creative activity in general. Thus even if my larger philosophical notions and visions of the future turn out to be wrong, or my formulation of them proves to have been incompetent, at least these first four chapters are likely to give my readers what, without feigned modesty, I believe to be a reasonably competent but brief account of one of the most important scientific developments of this century.

In the fifth chapter I will finally come to the main point, where I shall discuss the nature of progress. In particular, I shall attempt to show that, for more than one reason, progress is self-limiting. Chief among these reasons is that progress eventually prevents the perpetuation of its own mainspring, namely of what Nietzsche called the will to power, and that found its epitome in what Oswald Spengler called Faustian Man. I shall also trace the history of the *Idea of Progress*, which many people mistakenly believe to be one of high antiquity, or of universality, or of both, when, in fact, the Idea of Progress first arose less than two centuries ago in post-Enlightenment Europe. In the sixth chapter, I shall examine the present state of the main indexes to progress, the arts and sciences. Here I will try to demonstrate that the arts and sciences have now reached the end of their evolution. As far as the arts are concerned, the point of departure of my exposition will *not* be the Philistine premise that the arts have gone to the dogs because such contemporary manifestations as action painting or chance music are perversions of the hallowed tradition of Western art. On the contrary, I will follow the arguments made by some expert students of these problems, which show that artistic evolution has now gone as far as it can possibly go, precisely *because* of the legitimacy of contemporary painting and music. Showing that the sciences are also approaching their end requires somewhat of a *tour de force*, for which, moreover, I seem to be rather more on my own. In my seventh and final chapter I shall outline my notions of the nature of the Golden Age that lies ahead for us.

Almost everyone has recognized lately that universal leisure will be the most striking attribute of the future human condition. But in trying to envisage the portents of the coming leisure age, few futurologists seem to reckon with the disappearance of Faustian Man from that scene, the only character to whom the problem of leisure is actually relevant. It is my belief that the paradisiacal conditions extant not long ago in Faust-free Polynesia may serve as a fair prospectus of the Golden Age. The history of Polynesia shows in an exemplary way the nature of the social and psychological conditions that arise in a people who have acceded to economic security—either through abundant fruit provided without stint by felicitous nature in the South Seas or by automated technology in these parts. I will try to show that adaptation to this Polynesian future has already progressed to an obvious degree in our very midst.

On first sight, the finding that progress in general and creative activity in particular are now reaching their ends might appear to reflect a deeply pessimistic outlook on the future, a typical product of Nuclear Age *Weltschmerz*. On second sight, however, it must become apparent that my conclusions are, if anything, optimistic, since I shall show that just at that very moment in history when the possibilities for future progress and creative exertion are becoming exhausted, the secular consequences of past progress have given rise to a human psyche which is perfectly adapted to that entirely novel condition. This view is, therefore, in harmony with the precepts of Voltaire's Doctor Pangloss, since where else could such amazingly felicitous concord have occurred but in the best of possible worlds?

PART I

THE RISE AND FALL
OF MOLECULAR GENETICS

"Wie an dem Tag, der dich der Welt verliehen,
Die Sonne stand zum Grusse der Planeten
Bist alsobald und fort und fort gediehen
Nach dem Gesetz, wonach du angetreten."

GOETHE

The Hapsburg Lip. Inheritance of a Royal Mutant Gene through the Centuries. *Upper left:* Maximilian I (1459–1519). (By permission of The Bettmann Archive); *upper right:* Maximilian's grandson, Charles V (1500–58) (by permission of The Bettmann Archive); *lower left:* Archduke Charles of Teschen (1771–1847) (by permission of The Picture Archives of the Austrian National Library); *lower right:* Teschen's son, Archduke Albrecht (1817–95) (by permission of The Picture Archives of the Austrian National Library).

1. THE CLASSIC PERIOD

One summer evening in 1965, an enormous crowd, probably the largest ever in its six-hundred-year history, packed the Church of the Assumption in the Moravian town of Brno, to celebrate a memorial mass for Gregor Mendel, onetime abbot of the Augustinian monastery to which that church had formerly belonged. It was not so much piety for departed prelates that had brought together the members of that largely noncommunicant crowd, but rather the wish to pay homage to the memory of their founder. For in Mendel's own church was then gathered an ecumenical body of geneticists, who had come to Brno from all parts of the world at the invitation of the Czechoslovak Academy of Sciences to commemorate the one-hundredth anniversary of their science, which was founded there in 1865, on the day that Mendel presented his paper, "Experiments on Plant Hybrids," before the Brno Society of Natural Science. In view of its timing, locale, and auspices, this rite served also as a Te Deum for the official resurrection of genetics and the rehabilitation of geneticists in the Soviet Union and Eastern Europe, after nearly two decades of suppression of "Mendelism-Morganism" by the once politically influential and then recently deposed agronomist Trofim Lysenko. But this memorial mass could have been thought to have had yet another symbolic meaning: a commencement exercise for the students of heredity, who had begun their work, not a century ago, but ten thousand years earlier in neolithic times, and whose quest for the understanding of how like begets like was now about to reach its goal.

For the capacity of living organisms to pass on their own qualities to their offspring is so obvious that the recognition of heredity no doubt ranks as one of man's earliest scientific observations. Indeed, it was precisely this recognition and the realization of the possibility of selective breeding that enabled the Stone Age denizens of the Near East to develop some of our domestic animals and crop plants from wild prototypes. This first success in biotechnology brought about the dawn of civilization, the transition from nomadic, food-gathering to sedentary, agricultural-urban societies in the Fertile Crescent in about 8000 B.C. The practical know-how gathered in millennia of breeding experience was passed on as magical or religious canon, as for example, in the biblical stricture "Thou shalt not let thy cattle gender with a diverse kind; thou shalt not sow thy field with mingled seed." By classical times, breeding rules were being applied to human stock as well, such as the infanticide of defective offspring practiced in the Greek city-states.

The philosophers of classical Greece, particularly Hippocrates and later Aristotle, gave some thought to hereditary processes, some of their views being surprisingly astute, and others now seeming less brilliant. One of Aristotle's notions that seems most extravagant to us now concerns descriptions of fantastic hybrid matings between wildly different animal species. He thought, for instance, that a cross between a camel and a leopard had spawned the giraffe, and eels came ashore to mate with snakes, notions which persisted throughout the Middle Ages and even until after the Renaissance. Probably the most astute insight of the ancients was that heredity cannot be a simple matter: It was noted that a child resembles sometimes the father, sometimes the mother, sometimes both parents and sometimes only a grandparent. As far as animal husbandry was concerned, rules and prescriptions of classical times for selection and breeding of stock were not significantly improved until the rise of genetics in the nineteenth century. The Ancients must, therefore, have been in possession of *some* of the principles of heredity. But little progress in the understanding of heredity was made in the next two millennia. The Renaissance, which had initiated the re-awakening of interest and rejection of dogmatic superstition in the physical sciences, still left heredity relatively untouched. Not until Mendel provided his radically new insights did the new era dawn in which the mechanisms governing the self-reproduction of man and his fellow creatures became ultimately revealed.

For his "Experiments on Plant Hybrids" Mendel cultivated in the garden of his Brno monastery various strains of garden peas differing in seed morphology and color. He crossed these pea strains and observed the frequencies of various seed types both among first-generation progeny plants produced by crosses of the parental strains, and among second-generation progeny plants produced by crosses of the first-generation progeny. These crosses revealed striking statistical regularities in the frequency of transmission of the parental characteristics. From these statistical results, in a piece of brilliant deduction that must be placed among the most astute intellectual contributions to our understanding of nature, Mendel inferred that hereditary characteristics are carried and passed on to the progeny as discrete units. Each plant carries a homologous pair of such units, of which one is selected at random for transmission to any progeny individual. Mendel's insights were, however, still too advanced for his times, and the publication of his results and conclusions in the *Journal of the Brno Society of Natural Science* remained unnoticed by the community of biologists for another thirty-five years. Charles Darwin, Mendel's most illustrious contemporary biologist, who had gained immediate fame for his theory of evolution, was never aware of Mendel's discovery of the hereditary units on which the natural selection propounded by Darwin actually operates. Indeed, Darwin's "pangenesis" concept of the mechanism of heredity, namely that each part of the adult organism produces something which is collected in the "seed" for transmission to the offspring, was more or less the same as that propounded by Hippocrates some twenty-three centuries earlier.

In the meantime, while Mendel's discovery lay dormant on the dusty shelves of some 120 libraries now known to have received

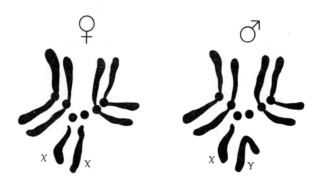

The four pairs of chromosomes of female (♀) and male (♂) Drosophila fruit flies. The pair on the bottom represents the sex chromosomes, of which the female carries two of type X and of which the male carries one of type X and one of type Y. (From H. Curtis, *Biology*, Worth Publishers, New York [1968].)

the rather obscure journal in which he published his results, the problem of the hereditary mechanism was being attacked from another direction. By about 1870, microscopic studies of the mechanism of fertilization of eggs by sperm had led to the recognition that the cell nucleus must be the seat of the hereditary material. At about the time of Mendel's death, in 1884, Wilhelm Roux had inferred that the hereditary material is not the *whole* nucleus, but the threadlike nuclear particles, or *chromosomes*. For Roux reasoned that the doubling and the longitudinal splitting of the chromosomes and the manner of their subsequent distribution among daughter nuclei in cell division satisfy what he imagined to be the requirements for the comportment of the hereditary material. Roux's ideas were quickly adopted by August Weissmann and elaborated into a complete theory of heredity and development. Weissmann proposed that in sexually reproducing, multicellular organisms, the number of chromosomes is halved in the formation of egg and sperm cells. The original number of chromosomes is then restored upon fusion of the nuclei of egg and sperm in the fertilization process, to give rise to a new individual, whose hereditary material is half of paternal and half of maternal provenance. These insights now provided a rational basis for repeating the kind of quantitative breeding experiments Mendel had already done, and in 1900 three botanists, Hugo de Vries, Carl Correns, and Erich von Tschermak independently rediscovered both Mendel's laws of inheritance and his by then thirty-five-year-old paper.

Upon the rediscovery of Mendel's work, genetics came into blossom (and was given its name), in the first four decades of this century, during which time an impressive body of knowledge was amassed. In a first stage of this development, the Mendelian unit of heredity was further clarified conceptually and named the *gene;* the possibility of sudden, permanent change in the character of the gene was recognized, a process which was called *mutation;* and Mendelian analysis of inheritance was shown to be applicable not only to plants, but also to animals, including man. One age-old problem that had intrigued natural philosophers since antiquity found its solution at about that time: the mechanism of sex determination. For it was discovered then that maleness or femaleness is transmitted to the progeny as any other Mendelian unit, the sex of an organism depending upon which combination of two kinds of special sex chromosomes were present in the particular egg and sperm whose union gave rise to an individual.

A second stage of this development began in 1910, when T. H. Morgan turned to the study of the genetics of the fruit fly Drosophila. With this experimental material, Morgan and his pupils established clearly during the next few years that the random assortment of different pairs of homologous parental genes among progeny individuals observed by Mendel and his rediscoverers obtains only for genes which reside on separate chromosomes. Genes which reside on the same chromosome, and are thus *linked*, were shown to be generally transmitted together. Such linked genes can, however, be separated by the process of *crossing over*. Crossing over occurs during the halving of the chromosome complement prior to formation of the sperm in the male or of the egg in the female, the probability of separation of two linked genes in the progeny being inversely related to the

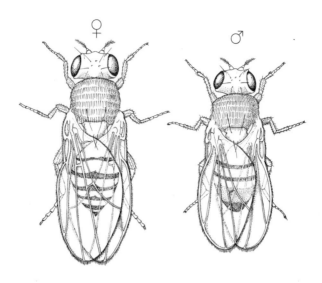

Female (♀) and male (♂) Drosophila fruit flies. (From H. Curtis, *Biology*, Worth Publishers, New York [1968].)

nearness, or *linkage*, of their positions on the same chromosome. Thus, on the basis of the frequency of separation of linked genes among the brood of genetically marked Drosophila parents, Morgan and his school established a *genetic map* of the four pairs of homologous Drosophila chromosomes. This map indicated the relative chromosomal locations of the then known Drosophila genes.

Morgan's work brought about nearly universal acceptance of the Mendelian principles of heredity, though pockets of resistance to these views remained extant until very recent times, mainly among ideologically encumbered biologists and naïve plant and animal breeders. This acceptance paved the way for the third stage of this development, during which great advances were made in the understanding of the mechanics of heredity, at the levels of individual cells, multicellular organisms, and populations. These advances, in turn, paved the way for theoretical insights, such as a quantitative analysis of the dynamics of organic evolution, and brought forth tremendous practical benefits to agriculture and medicine. As far as agriculture was concerned,

Mendelian principles had at last made possible rational rather than rule-of-thumb breeding procedures. And through these procedures new varieties of traditional crop plants and domestic animals possessing economically important properties such as disease resistance, higher yield, capacity to grow in unfavorable climes and, more recently, toughness suitable for mechanical harvest, were produced. These successes in biotechnology were an important factor in bringing about the enormous reduction in the fraction of the population of industrially advanced countries that is now engaged in producing the food that the rest consumes. As far as medicine was concerned, the recognition of the genetic basis of many human disorders and diseases provided a rationale for taking measures for their prevention or relief.

During this entire development, however, the fundamental unit of genetics, the gene remained an abstract, formal concept, largely devoid of any physical content. The line of study that ultimately *was* to reveal the material basis of the gene actually began within two or three years of Mendel's discovery of it, though more than eighty years were to elapse before the connection was made. In the late 1860s, the Swiss chemist F. Miescher isolated a hitherto unknown, phosphorus-rich, acidic substance both from the nuclei of pus cells and from salmon sperm. This novel substance came to be called *nucleic acid*, a name that turned out to be misleading but has been retained. After the ubiquitous presence of nucleic acid in plant and animal kingdoms was demonstrated, the turn-of-the-century biochemist A. Kossel identified the building blocks of nucleic acid as four nitrogenous bases, *adenine* and *guanine* (the purines) and *cytosine* and *uracil* (the pyrimidines); *phosphoric acid;* and a five-carbon sugar. By the 1920s, further analytical work had shown that there exist two basically different kinds of nucleic acid: *ribonucleic acid,* or *RNA,* and *deoxyribonucleic acid,* or *DNA.* RNA contains *ribose*, whereas DNA contains *deoxyribose* as its sugar. DNA, furthermore, does not contain uracil; instead it contains *thymine,* a compound very similar to uracil. Nitrogenous base, sugar, and phosphoric acid are linked together to form a *nucleotide.* By the 1930s it had been shown that nucleic acid molecules contain sev-

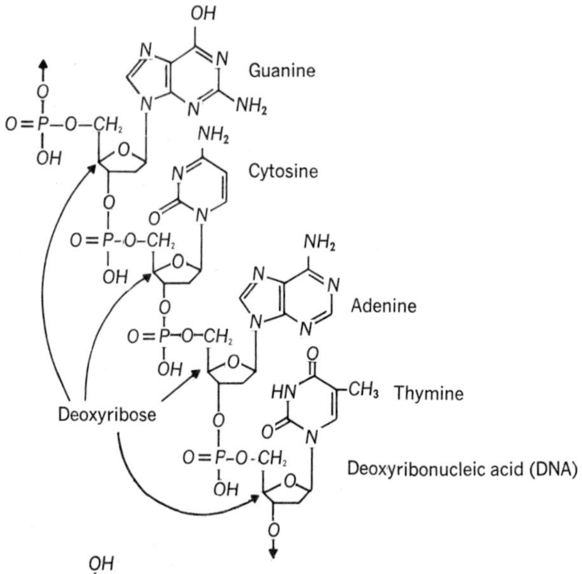

Deoxyribonucleic acid (DNA)

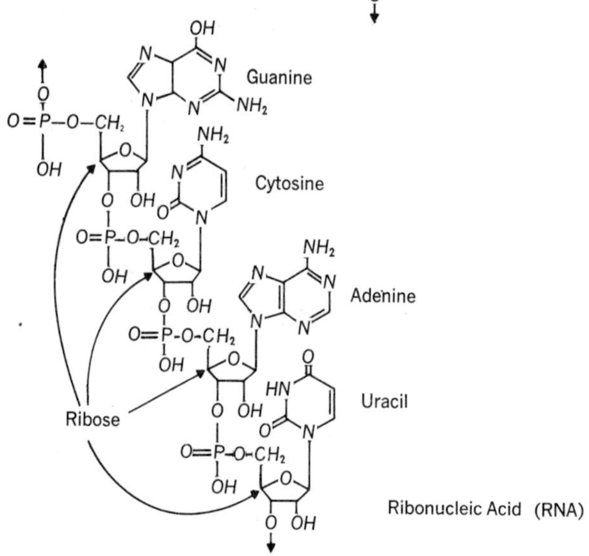

Ribonucleic Acid (RNA)

eral such nucleotides linked through phosphate diester bonds between their sugars, but another ten years elapsed before the enormous high molecular weight of the nucleic acids was finally appreciated. As we now know, nucleic acid molecules consist of thousands, and sometimes millions of nucleotides strung together in long chains. That nucleic acid probably has *some* connection with hereditary processes was realized as soon as chemical observations revealed that DNA is a major constituent of the chromosomes. But though the idea that nucleic acid might be *the* hereditary material had been proposed already at the turn of the century, it was not given serious consideration by many students of genetics before the experiments that proved this to be the case were finally done many years later.

The nature of the gene thus remained unknown throughout this period. Besides not having fathomed its chemical structure, geneticists had been unable to explain how the gene manages to preside over specific cellular physiological processes from its nuclear throne or how it manages to achieve its own faithful replication in the cellular reproductive cycle. As late as 1950, in an essay written on the golden jubilee of the rediscovery of Mendel's work, Drosophila geneticist H. J. Muller, by then one of the elder statesmen of genetics and a leading philosopher of the gene, spoke of this state of affairs as follows: ". . . the real core of genetic theory still appears to lie in the deep unknown. That is, we have as yet no actual knowledge of the mechanism underlying that unique property which makes a gene a gene—its ability to cause the synthesis of another structure like itself, in which even the mutations of the original gene are copied. . . . What must happen is that just that precise reaction is *selectively* caused to occur, out of a virtually infinite series of possible reactions, whereby materials taken from a common medium become synthetized into a pattern just like that of the structure which itself guides the reaction. We do not know of such things yet in chemistry." Yet, despite the lack of understanding of its "real core," genetics *had* been fantastically successful. It had raised our understanding of the living world to previously unknown heights of sophistication.

The developments that I have so far traced out in the briefest form and the body of knowledge which they produced is generally called *classical* genetics nowadays, though this epithet is not relished by those of my colleagues who still continue this tradition today, and who, not unnaturally, resent the implication that their work is "classical" rather than "modern." But I think that it is not altogether inappropriate to reserve a special name for this period of genetic research, since there is one very important aspect that characterizes pre-1940 genetics and sets it apart from the "modern" genetics that was to follow in its wake: *For classical genetics, the gene is an indivisible, formal, and abstract unit.* Study of the detailed nature and physical identity of the gene, though undoubtedly of great intellectual interest for the classical geneticist, is not an essential part of his work. His theories on the mechanics of heredity and the experimental predictions to which these theories lead are largely formal, and their success does not depend on knowledge of structures at the submicroscopic, or molecular, level where the genes lie. By 1940, classical genetics had reached its apogee, since solutions for most of its basic problems were now at hand. Classical genetics then changed from a heroic phase, in which men addressed themselves to hitherto unfathomable questions, to an academic phase, in which a wealth of detail, albeit most important detail, was worked on by an army of competent scholars and technologists following well-established lines. The period of trail-blazing was over, though most of the practical benefits were yet to be reaped. The name "classical" for pre-1940 genetics probably derives from an analogy with turn-of-the-century classical physics, whose fundamental and unfathomed unit, the atom, had similarly allowed very far-reaching insights into the macroscopic properties of matter. The analogy between classical genetics and classical physics, like most analogies, is possibly more obscurantist than luminary, but the parallel between these two disciplines is nevertheless striking.

In order to extend the scope of genetics beyond its classical frame of reference of the indivisible gene, the gap between chemistry and genetics, the complementary avenues to the study of living matter, had to be bridged. Conscious efforts in this direction began in the late 1930s when it was shown that certain Drosophila mutants owe their characteristic eye color to an inability to carry out some particular step in the biochemical synthetic sequence of the brown pigment which endows the normal fly with its red eye color. Since each reaction step of that sequence is catalyzed by a particular enzyme, it seemed plausible to infer that the eye color genes of Drosophila control the formation of enzymes of eye color pigment synthesis and that mutation of a gene engenders loss of formation of an enzyme of that reaction sequence. It should be noted, incidentally, that the abolition of formation of specific enzymes by gene mutation was actually first discovered not in flies but in man, by A. E. Garrod, who coined the phrase "inborn errors of metabolism" in 1909, after he showed that alkaptonuria, an arthritic condition accompanied by the excretion of black urine, is clearly a hereditary human disease. But Garrod's findings, like those of Mendel, seemed to be so far ahead of their time that they had little influence in the marketplace of genetic ideas until their rediscovery thirty years later.

In 1940, G. W. Beadle and E. L. Tatum, who had played an important part in the elucidation of the genetic control of the Drosophila eye pigment synthesis but had become discouraged over the difficulties encountered in that material, turned their attention to the biochemical genetics of a microorganism, the bread mold Neurospora. According to Beadle: "With the new organism our approach could be basically different. Through control of the constituents of the culture medium we could search for mutations in genes concerned with the synthesis of already known chemical substances of biological importance. We soon found ourselves with so many mutant strains unable to synthesize vitamins, amino acids, and other essential components of protoplasm that we could not decide which ones to work on first." In the next five years, Beadle, Tatum, and their collaborators did manage to analyze the genetic and biochemical characteristics of a sufficient number of their Neurospora mutants to lend strong support to the "one gene-one enzyme" theory. This theory states that each gene has only one primary function, which in most or all cases is to direct the synthesis of one and only one enzyme, and thus to control one single chemical reaction catalyzed by that one enzyme. Though the idea that genes control single functions was not really original with Beadle and

Tatum, their clear formulation and strong experimental evidence in favor of the one gene-one enzyme theory had a profound impact on subsequent thought about the central problem of genetics. For the belief that in presiding over cellular function each gene is doing only one thing gave hope of ultimately finding out what that one thing might actually be. This hope was to be realized through the developments I shall describe in the next two chapters.

Classical genetics is thus the first example that I bring up for consideration in these chapters of how an age-old domain of human inquiry experiences at first a very slow development over millennia and centuries, then speeds up its rate of progress, and finally brings about the solution of the problems posed by its frame of reference. At this stage, the field changes in character, since its very success has made it a less attractive arena for romantic strife. The field has now lost its appeal for the kind of person who is driven to explore uncharted territory. Scholars and technologists replace the knights-errant and work out the details and the applications. For their part, the romantics now try to extend, or even abandon, the classical frame of reference, and presently create a "modern" successor field. The point that I shall try to make in later chapters is that it is not reasonable to expect that this succession of classic and modern phases of any aspect of human endeavor will or even can occur indefinitely. For it seems to me most unreasonable to think that there are no limits to the extent to which the human intellect can extend its frame of reference.

Before closing this instant summary of classical genetics, I want to consider briefly one of its problem children, namely *eugenics*, that has raised much controversy hinging on important philosophical issues. Shortly before the turn of the century, and thus even before the proper start of classical genetics, the apocalyptic notion arose that civilization has an adverse effect on human evolution, in that medical technology makes possible survival of not only the fit but also of the unfit. In this way, the laboriously acquired, wonderful hereditary capital of humanity is evidently being squandered: For instance, the invention of eyeglasses renders inoperative the previous strong natural selection against genes determining defective vision. Thus it seemed to follow that unless some remedial action were undertaken, the human species could look forward to a steady biological deterioration, which would ultimately lead to its decline and possibly extinction. These views presently received strong reinforcement when, with the rise of human genetics, the genetic basis of many physiological and anatomical defects was actually demonstrated. It was but a short intellectual step to extend these considerations also to psychological attributes under presumptive genetic control, such as intelligence and criminality, and to envisage that the ever-increasing application of humanitarian procedures, such as social welfare and liberalized criminal laws, engenders also a behavioral deterioration of the human stock. The latter prospect was viewed as being particularly ominous in that so-called races or social subgroups thought to be of hereditarily inferior intellect or moral fiber are evidently reproducing more rapidly than their superior fellows, thanks to whose very efforts the inferior are escaping the rigors of Darwinian selection.

These thoughts led to the promulgation of eugenics by Francis Galton in the 1890s. Eugenics is a purposive, socioscientific human breeding program, which attempts not only to arrest the culturally generated putative hereditary degeneration of the human stock, but even aims to improve the physical and mental qualities of future generations. Although these ideas were first elaborated by perfectly respectable students of heredity who attempted to buttress their pleas for institution of eugenic procedures by more or less rational, though not always rigorous, observation and argument, eugenics proved to have an irresistible appeal to political cranks and racial bigots. The monstrous institution in Nazi Germany of the effort to protect Aryan "blood" from future contamination by that of the Jewish "race" made the contemplation of any large-scale eugenic programs, even by means less revolting than those employed in Germany, odious to most civilized people for some twenty years. But in the United States there have recently reappeared demands for a crash program application of eugenic methods to the solution of the problems of the American Negro community, whose socio-economic disadvantages, so it is supposed by the people who make such demands, derive in part from its hereditary patrimony (which, it might be noted, is about 30 percent European). Though it was perfectly well-known to the community of American geneticists that any such program would be completely pointless at this stage of our knowledge, it proved politically necessary to call a special conference of the leading students of human heredity to issue a manifesto exposing the wrong-headed and ill-informed nature of these demands.

In any case, the philosophical basis of eugenics is, of course, false, since the pseudo-Darwinian argument that civilization is fostering the survival of the "unfit" is clearly fallacious. As everybody now knows, "survival of the fittest" is nothing but the tautology "survival of the survivors," and hence in this connection "unfit" represents not an objective scientific but a subjective value judgment. It seems difficult to predict today to what extent eugenics is likely to be practiced tomorrow, but, through such current practices as genetic counseling of prospective parents and "banks" of sperm donated by "superior" fathers for artificial insemination, eugenics is, in fact, *already* a going, albeit limited, concern. The insights brought by molecular genetics, to be considered in the next three chapters, have meanwhile given rise to talk of a eugenics of the future operating not merely by the "classical" method of selecting favorable hereditary traits for breeding from an existing gene pool but by tailor-making the desired genetic molecules directly. An even more fantastic eugenic prospect appears to be the *vegetative* propagation of humans. For our present, albeit as yet incomplete, understanding of the ontogenetic processes that lead from the fertilized egg to the development of the mature man do not exclude the possibility of an artificial regeneration of the whole individual from one of his body cells. If such regeneration were to prove feasible, an indefinitely large number of individuals could be made to arise, all of whom would be identical "twins" of the same genetic constitution as the "perfect" donor person.

Joshua Lederberg has recently pointed out that in the immediate future *euphenics* is likely to be of much greater importance in affecting the human condition than eugenics. Euphenics addresses itself to the task of modifying the *expression* of the human genes rather than their intrinsic character, and hence operates here and now rather than on future generations. Unlike eugenics, euphenics *is* already in full swing, through such procedures as immunization against infectious diseases, administration of hormones, and transplantation and implantation of natural and artificial organs. Rapid advances in euphenic medical technology are not difficult to envisage at present. For instance, at the outset of life, superior babies with better brains and bodies are likely to be born by manipulation of the intrauterine environment, and the end of life may be indefinitely delayed by replacement or rejuvenation of worn-out organs and tissues.

Thus eugenics and euphenics bid fair to bring about before very long the realization of one aspect of the Golden Age: Mortal men *will* soon be free from the miseries of old age, their legs and arms *will* never fail, and when they die, it *will* be as though they were overcome with sleep. But whether this Golden Age of genetically standardized, made-to-order and spare-part patchwork folk will be to the liking of the geneticists who toiled hard to bring it about is another matter. In another golden jubilee of genetics essay Julian Huxley wrote in defense of genetic engineering (of the civilized sort, naturally): "Once the fact is grasped that we men are agents of further evolution, and that there can be no action higher or more noble than the raising of the inherent possibilities of life as represented by the human species, then we shall somehow find ways and means for overcoming the resistances which stand in the way of our performing that part of our destiny and our duty." But nearly twenty years earlier, Julian's brother Aldous had already realized that the destiny of these high and noble actions is the Brave New World.

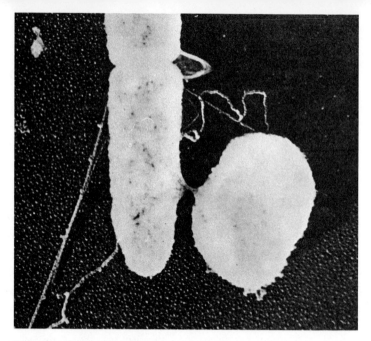

Electron micrograph of two conjugating *E. coli* bacteria. A slender connecting bridge has been formed between the elongated male bacterium and the rotund female bacterium. DNA passes from donor to recipient cell through this bridge. (Photograph provided by Thomas F. Anderson.)

Electron micrograph and interpretative cartoon of a bacteriophage active on *E. coli*. The head contains DNA and the tail is the organ by means of which the particle becomes attached to the cell wall of its host bacterium. (Photograph provided by Edouard Kellenberger.)

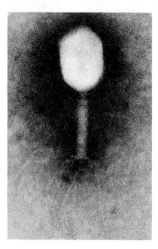
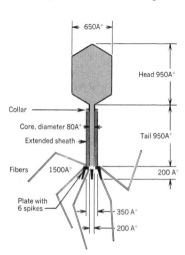

2. THE ROMANTIC PERIOD

We saw in the preceding chapter that upon the rediscovery of Mendel's laws and papers at the turn of this century genetics came into flower. During the next four decades an impressive body of knowledge was amassed which finally brought the understanding of the mechanisms of heredity that had puzzled students of nature since the beginnings of science. I referred to this body of knowledge as "classical" *genetics*, whose hallmark was that its fundamental concept, the gene, remained an indivisible, formal, and abstract unit. For neither the chemical nature of the gene nor the processes by which it presides over the physiological reactions that cause like to beget like had been fathomed. By 1940, however, a new era was dawning. The "one gene-one enzyme" theory had been promulgated. According to that theory, each gene has only one primary function, namely to direct the synthesis of one single enzyme. This enzyme, in turn, catalyzes one single chemical reaction. This very great, and at the time rather daring, conceptual simplification brought the hope that the seemingly hopelessly complex governance of physiological processes might ultimately be understood in chemical terms.

At about this time, a new crew, rather different in formation and motivation from the classical geneticists, began to take an interest in the nature of the gene. Most of these newcomers had little or no acquaintance with the body of genetic knowledge accumulated in the preceding decades, nor even with biology in general. Their training lay mainly in the physical sciences and their interest was confined largely to solving one and only one problem: the physical basis of heredity. There was nothing new, of course, in the phenomenon of physical scientists addressing themselves to the solution of biological problems; indeed, many of the greatest contributions to nineteenth-century biology had been made by men trained in the physical sciences. Pasteur, Helmholtz, and Mendel himself had been physical scientists. But there was a rather special philosophical twist that informed the men responsible for this particular development of the 1940s. For just when old-fashioned vitalism (the eighteenth-century doctrine which held that, in the last analysis, the phenomena of life can only be explained by a mysterious "vital force," neither physical nor chemical in nature) was rapidly disappearing from intellectually enlightened circles, the idea that some biological phenomena might turn out to be *not* accountable wholly in terms of conventional physical concepts was fashioned by Niels Bohr. In the wake of the formulation of the quantum theory of atomic structure, Bohr developed the more general notion that the impossibility of describing the quantum of action, and hence what he called its "irrationality" from the purview of classical physics, is but a heuristic paradigm of how the encounter of what appears to be a deep paradox eventually leads to a higher level of understanding. He presented these views in his address "Light and Life" before the International Congress of Light Therapy in 1932. "At first, this situation [i.e., the introduction of an irrational element] might appear very deplorable; but, as has often happened in the history of science, when new discoveries have revealed an essential limitation of ideas the universal applicability of which had never been disputed, we have been rewarded by getting a wider view and a greater power of correlating phenomena which before might even have appeared contradictory." In particular, Bohr thought it would be well to keep this possibility in mind in the study of life: "The recognition of the essential importance of fundamentally atomistic features in the functions of living organisms is by no means sufficient for a comprehensive explanation of biological phenomena. The question at issue, therefore, is whether some fundamental traits are still missing in the analysis of natural phenomena, before we can reach an understanding of life on the basis of physical experience." The difficulty inherent in trying to understand life in physical terms is, according to Bohr, "that the conditions holding for biological and physical researches are not directly comparable, since the necessity of keeping the object of investigation alive imposes a restriction on the former, which finds no counterpart in the latter. Thus we should doubtless kill an animal if we tried to carry the investigation of its organs so far that we could describe the role played by single atoms in vital functions." Thus there seems to exist for the living animal an "uncertainty principle" formally analogous to that of the electron, in that "there must remain an uncertainty as regards the physical condition to which [the organism is] subjected, and the idea suggests itself that the minimal freedom we must allow the organism in this respect is just large enough to hide its ultimate secrets from us. On this view, the existence of life must be considered as an elementary fact that cannot be explained, but must be taken as a starting point in biology, in a similar way as the quantum of action, which appears as an irrational element from the point of view of classical mechanical physics, taken together with the existence of the elementary particles, forms the foundation of atomic physics. The asserted impossibility of a physical or chemical explanation of the function peculiar to life would in this sense be analogous to the insufficiency of the mechanical analysis for the understanding of the stability of atoms." These ideas of Bohr would evidently put the relation of physics to biology on a new footing.

That genetics was, in fact, a domain of biological inquiry in which physical and chemical explanations might turn out to be "insufficient" in Bohr's sense was spelled out in 1935 by Bohr's pupil Max Delbrück. In a paper entitled "On the Nature of Gene Mutation and Gene Structure" Delbrück points out that "whereas in physics all measurements must in principle be traced back to measurements of place and time, there is hardly a case in which the fundamental concept of genetics, the character difference, can be expressed meaningfully in terms of absolute units." Thus, Delbrück thought, one could take the view "that genetics is autonomous and must not be mixed up with physico-chemical conceptions." Admittedly, "the refined [genetic] analysis of [the fruit fly] *Drosophila* has led to [estimates of] gene sizes which are comparable to those of the largest known molecules endowed with a specific structure. This result has led many investigators to consider that the genes are nothing else than a particular kind of molecule, except that their detailed structure is not yet known." But, Delbrück continued, one must keep in mind that there exists here a significant departure from the chemical definition of the molecule. "In chemistry we speak of a certain kind of molecule when we are faced with a substance which reacts uniformly to chemical stimulation. In genetics, however, we have by definition only a single representative of the relevant 'gene molecule,' in a chemically heterogeneous environment; and we ascertain its identity with a gene of another individual only on the basis of its similar onto-genetic effect. Thus there could be no question of a uniform chemical reaction, not even in a Gedankenexperiment, unless we conceive of the relevant gene as being isolated from a large number of genetically identical organisms and would make a chemical study of the behavior of the ensemble of these isolated genes." In any case, the main reason for thinking of the gene as a molecule in the first place is its evident long-term *stability* in the face of outside influences. "Hence, when we speak of [genes as] molecules we are not so much thinking of their similar behavior but more generally of a well-defined union of atoms, supposing that the identity of two genes represents the same stable arrangement of the same atoms. The stability of this configuration must be especially great *vis-à-vis* the chemical reactions that normally proceed in the living cell; the genes can participate in general metabolism only catalytically." This stability, Delbrück thought, could be accounted for only if each atom making up the gene "molecule" were fixed in its mean position and electronic state, so that only discontinuous, saltatory changes could occur in this arrangement, whenever an atom of the ensemble happened to acquire an energy superior to the activation energy required to change its particular state. These changes evidently would correspond to gene mutations.

In 1945, immediately after the conclusion of World War II, a little book appeared which popularized these hitherto rather esoteric views and secured for them a much wider audience. This was *What is Life?* by Erwin Schrödinger, then living as an anti-Nazi emigré in Ireland. In this book Schrödinger heralded the dawn of a new epoch in biological research to his fellow physicists, whose knowledge of biology was generally confined to a stale botanical and zoological lore. Having one of the inventors of quantum mechanics put the question "What is life?" now provided for physicists an authoritative confrontation with a fundamental problem worthy of their mettle. Since many of these physical scientists were suffering in the immediate postwar period from a general professional malaise, they were eager to direct their efforts toward a new frontier which, according to Schrödinger, was now ready for some exciting developments. In thus stirring up the passions of this audience, Schrödinger's book became a kind of *Uncle Tom's Cabin* of the revolution in biology that, when the dust had cleared, left molecular genetics as its legacy.

Schrödinger opens with the comforting statement that "the obvious inability of present-day physics and chemistry to account [for the events that take place in a living organism] is no reason at all for doubting that they can be accounted for by those sciences." Since, as Schrödinger points out next, organisms are large compared to atoms, there is no reason why they should not obey exact physical laws. And even the peculiar quality of living matter, namely that it creates order out of disorder, does not put it beyond the pale of thermodynamics, whose Second Law asserts that in the universe order decays into disorder. For life on earth evidently feeds on the gigantic decay processes occurring in the sun and is thus no more in violation of the Second Law than are rain clouds made up from water that sunlight has distilled from the oceans. No, the *real* problem in want of an explanation is the physical basis of genetic information. For while the genes are evidently responsible for the order that an organism manifests, *their* dimensions are not so very large compared to atoms. How then do the genes resist the fluctuations to which they should be subject? How, wonders Schrödinger, has the tiny gene of the Habsburg lip managed to preserve its specific structure, and hence its information content, for centuries while being maintained at a temperature 310° above absolute zero? Following Delbrück's then ten-year-old proposal that this stability derives from the atoms of the gene "molecule" staying put in "energy wells," Schrödinger proposes that genes are able to preserve their structures because the chromosome that carries them is an *aperiodic crystal*. This large aperiodic crystal is composed of a succession of a small number of isomeric elements, the exact nature of the succession representing the *hereditary code*. Schrödinger illustrates the vast combinatorial possibilities of such a code with an example that uses the two symbols of the Morse code as its isomeric elements. He thinks that "we may safely assert that there is no alternative to [Delbrück's] molecular explanation of the hereditary substance. The physical aspect leaves no other possibility to account for its permanence. If the Delbrück picture should fail, we would have to give up further attempts." Furthermore, "from Delbrück's general picture of the hereditary substance it emerges that living matter, while not eluding the 'laws of physics' as established up to date, is likely to involve hitherto unknown 'other laws of physics,' which, however, once they have been revealed will form just as integral a part of this science as the former."

The philosophy of the search for "other laws" was spelled out in further detail by Delbrück in a lecture he gave in 1949 entitled "A Physicist Looks at Biology." Delbrück, first of all, calls attention to what he believes to be a fundamental difference between physics and biology. Whereas the aim of physics is to discover universal laws, biologists cannot reasonably aspire to any such aim, since "any one cell, embodying as it does the record of a billion years of evolution, represents more a historical than a physical event. . . . You cannot expect to explain so wise an old bird in a few simple words." After discussing the relation of classical physics to quantum physics as an object lesson for biology, Delbrück states Bohr's (and his) belief that "just as we find features of the atom—its stability, for instance—which are not reducible to mechanics, we may find features of the living cell which are not reducible to atomic physics, but whose appearance stands in a *complementary* relation to those of atomic physics." Delbrück admits that he is aware that these views might be considered as being very dangerous, since they are susceptible to naïve misinterpretation and could inspire either unnecessary defeatism or wild and unreasonable vitalistic speculations. Nevertheless, he asserts that they can be justified on the grounds that the suggestion of a complementarity situation in biology has been the prime motive for the interest in biology of "at least *one* physicist." Delbrück concludes his lecture with a homily that accounts for the at first sight surprising deprecation of biochemistry by the physicist-geneticists. Biochemistry, Delbrück said, is not likely to be very useful for gaining an understanding of the really important matters in biology: "He (the physicist) may be told that the only real access of atomic physics is through biochemistry. Listening to the story of modern biochemistry, he might become persuaded that the cell is a sack full of enzymes acting on the substrates converting them through various intermediate stages either into cell substance or into waste products. . . . The enzymes must be situated in their proper strategic positions to perform their duties in a well-regulated fashion. They in turn must be synthesized and must be brought into position by maneuvers which are not yet understood, but which, at first sight at least, do not necessarily seem to differ in nature from the rest of biochemistry. . . . And yet this program of explaining the simple through the complex smacks suspiciously of the program of explaining atoms in terms of complex mechanical models. It looks sane until paradoxes crop up and come into sharper focus, and this will not happen until the behavior of living cells has been carried into far greater detail. This analysis should be done on the cell's own terms, and theories should be formulated without fear of contradicting molecular physics. I believe that it is in this direction that physicists will show the greatest zeal and will create a new intellectual approach to biology which would lend meaning to the ill-used term 'biophysics.' "

It is because of the quixotic expectation to encounter "other" laws in the study of the gene that I am referring to the next development in genetic research that began in about 1940 as the *romantic period*. For the hope of fathoming the unfathomed through encounter of deep paradoxes is surely a romantic notion that sets its believers apart from cool schoolmen. It is to be noted, incidentally, that in Copenhagen, its ideological fountainhead, this notion wells deeper than from the mind of Bohr. Nearly a century before him, Bohr's fellow townsman Søren Kierkegaard had already extolled the search for the paradox: "Paradox is the passion of thought; and the thinker who is without paradox is like a lover without passion—an inconsiderable fellow."

In the course of the romantic period, the fruit fly Drosophila lost its hegemony as the star organism of experimental genetics and came to be replaced by bacteria and bacterial viruses. For, even though Drosophila had proven itself to be an ideal experimental material for solving the problems of classical genetics, its generation time of the order of weeks is still too long, and the thousands of its individuals that can be manipulated in any single experiment are still too few to have allowed study of extremely rare genetic events. And just such rare events provide essential clues to the molecular basis of heredity.

Bacteria, we might recall here, are the smallest of living cells. Their linear dimensions of 0.0001 cm place them just at the limits of resolution of the most powerful microscopes employing ordinary, visible light. Bacteria contain almost all of the chemical compounds and carry out almost all of the metabolic reactions characteristic of higher organisms. One great advantage of bacteria as experimental material over such higher organisms as Drosophila is that many bacterial species proliferate on very simple and chemically completely defined substrates. Thus some bacteria can grow on a wholly synthetic medium that contains, in addition to water and simple salts, the sugar glucose as its only food source. From these simple substrates, such bacteria can home-make the complex ensemble of organic constituents that form the cell, such as carbohydrates, fats, proteins, and nucleic acids. Most higher organisms, in contrast, will not thrive on such simple substrates, since they cannot make all of their constituents from scratch. Bacteria grow by elongation. As soon as the cell has attained a critical length, it divides to produce two complete daughter individuals. The two daughter cells that result from this binary fission continue to grow at the same rate as their parent, and in due time again undergo binary fission to produce four granddaughter cells, which in their turn continue to grow and divide. Since the time elapsed between the moment of birth of a bacterial cell and its binary fission to produce its own two daughter cells can be as short as half an hour, it follows that within a single twenty-four hour day an experimenter can witness the appearance of member individuals of forty-eight successive generations. (At the rate of human reproduction, a comparable number of generations would take us back roughly to the time of Charlemagne.) At the end of these forty-eight generations a single parent bacterium will have given rise to no less than 2^{48} offspring, a number that is in the neighborhood of a million billion.

There exists in nature an immense diversity of bacteria, among which the pathogenic species, familiar because of their role in infectious diseases such as dysentery, tuberculosis, pneumonia, and diphtheria, represent but a tiny sample. The largest number of bacterial species by far are not pathogens; instead they live in soil and water and mud where they play a key role in the long-term maintenance of life, returning dead organic matter to the dust whence it came. Just as there was one fly, Drosophila, that dominated classical genetics, so there was one bacterium that was to become the darling of molecular genetics. This is the bacterium *Escherichia coli*, which happens to have the honor of inhabiting the human intestine. There billions of *E. coli* cells quietly carry out some of the exciting biochemical reactions which proceed in that organ. *E. coli* is not ordinarily pathogenic, a fortunate circumstance for molecular geneticists, whose ranks might otherwise have suffered decimation. It is fair to say that by now more details are known about *E. coli* than about any other cellular organism in all creation.

Tiny as they are, bacteria have their own parasites too, the even tinier bacterial viruses to which they can fall prey. Such bacterial viruses were discovered during the First World War, in England by F. W. Twort and in France by F. d'Hérelle. The latter gave them the name bacteriophages, or "eaters of bacteris." At the time, this discovery caused a sensation in the world of medical microbiology, because d'Hérelle promulgated the idea that bacteriophages are the chief agents of natural immunity against bacterial infections and should be most useful for a generalized therapy and prophylaxis. D'Hérelle could show that bacteriophages destroy the bacteria responsible for dysentery in the following manner: the virus particle first attaches itself to the surface of the dysentery bacterium, then penetrates into the interior of the cell, where it reproduces itself to generate an issue of many progeny viruses. These progeny are liberated and ready to infect further dysentery bacteria when the infected cell finally bursts open and dies. Thus it would be only necessary to cultivate in the laboratory large quantities of the *anti*dysentery bacteriophage and hold them in readiness for administration to a patient showing the first symptoms of the disease. Once in the body of the patient, the virus particles would seek out the dysentery bacteria, destroy them by multiplying at their expense, and thus cure the patient in the process. In fact, since the bacteriophages should be as transmissible from one person to the next as the dysentery bacteria, the virus-induced immunity should be as contagious as the disease itself. This previously undreamed-of way of ridding mankind of some of its most dreaded ills did not fail to fire the popular imagination as well, an aspect of the medical Zeitgeist of the 1920s preserved in Sinclair Lewis's novel *Arrowsmith*. Alas, plausible as this idea seemed at the outset, bacteriophages never *did* become a successful medical tool, in spite of twenty years of intensive work. And since in the meantime antibiotics have proven to be far more efficacious in the control of bacterial diseases than even D'Hérelle could have dared to hope for his panacea, that strange bacteriophage therapy chapter in the history of medicine can now be fairly considered as closed.

But despite the noisy fanfare on their behalf as the Great Hope of Universal Therapy and Prophylaxis, some farsighted people had soon realized that bacteriophages might represent a superb experimental material for studying the problems of heredity. As early as 1922, H. J. Muller wrote that "if these d'Hérelle bodies [i.e., bacteriophages] were really genes, fundamentally like our chromosome genes, they would give an utterly new angle from which to attack the gene problem." The same thought occurred to Delbrück when he was introduced to bacteriophages in 1938. By that time, practical interest in these viruses was already on the wane. Delbrück then decided to start experimenting on bacteriophages, in the expectation that study of their reproduction might bring a genetic paradox into focus. His work began with the design of the *one-step growth experiment*, utilizing as his experimental material a virus parasitic on *Escherichia coli*. The one-step growth experiment showed that each virus particle infecting an *E. coli* bacterium produces from one hundred to five hundred progeny particles after a brief half-hour *latent period*. Thus this experiment brought clearly into focus the central problem of biological replication. What is going on within the phage-infected bacterium during that half hour, while the parental virus particle manages to effect its own hundredfold replication? Surely, Delbrück thought, it should not be too difficult to answer this question when it is posed for a self-reproducing biological structure at a level of organization as simple as that of a virus. For in comparison to other organisms, even in comparison to its bacterial host cell, the bacteriophage *is* very simple. Its linear dimensions are only of the order of 0.00001 cm (that is, one-tenth the length of its bacterial host cell), and its weight is only about one-million billionth of a gram. It is made up of only two principal chemical components, present in roughly equal proportions: protein and deoxyribonucleic acid, or DNA. Its tiny size renders the bacteriophage invisible in any microscope employing ordinary, visible light, but upon the development of the much more powerful electron microscope in 1940 it became possible to obtain a direct visual image of the virus particle. These electron microphotographs showed that the virus consists of a head and a tail. It was presently established that the tail is composed of protein and that the head represents a stuffed bag, whose casing is protein and whose stuffing is DNA.

In 1940 Delbrück met Salvador Luria and Alfred Hershey, and this meeting engendered the origin of the American Phage Group. The members of this group were united by a single common goal, namely the desire to understand how during the half-hour latent period in the phage-infected cell there arise the one to five hundred copies of the proteinaceous tail and head structures and of the DNA complement of the parental virus particle. The initial growth of this group was rather slow, but after an annual missionary summer course at the Cold Spring Harbor Laboratory near New York City was organized to spread the new bacteriophage gospel among physicists and chemists, a more rapid growth set in. Nevertheless, by 1952, which was to be the last year of the romantic period, the Phage Group still numbered only three or four dozen people.

Delbrück, Luria, and Hershey dominated this romantic period, though during that period many other people, both within and without the Phage Group, had made discoveries that equaled in importance anything that these three had found. But, in my opinion at least, they then provided the main forward momentum for the quest for fathoming the nature of the gene, the spiritual hallmark of that romantic period. The main accomplishment of that period was the demonstration that, despite their very much smaller size and greater simplicity, bacteria and bacterial viruses do, in fact, manifest the same basic genetic phenomena as do the most complex higher organisms. Thus it was shown that the reproduction of both bacteriophages and bacteria is under the control of hereditary material which is organized in a linear array of genes formally analogous to the nuclear chromosomes of higher forms. These genes can undergo spontaneous mutation, a process that leads to the appearance of rare hereditary variants, or *mutant* viruses and bacteria. Most importantly, it was discovered that both viruses and bacteria manifest a primitive sort of sexual reproduction by means of which hybrid offspring result that have drawn some of their genes from one and some of their genes from the other of the two parents that engaged in the conjugal act. Indeed, it turned out that bacteria and their viruses represent one general genetic system, in that the process of crossing over can occur between the linear gene array of a virus and that of its bacterial host cell. Such "illegitimate" conjugal acts between the genetic structures of parasite and host were found to give rise to hybrid viruses that carry some bacterial genes and to hybrid bacteria that have incorporated some viral genes into their hereditary makeup.

In making a retrospective judgment, however, most geneticists would now agree that the most important discovery of the romantic period was made in 1944 by persons who had practically no connection at all with the Phage Group, namely by Oswald Avery and his collaborators. At that time, Avery found that upon addition of purified DNA extracted from normal *donor* bacteria to mutant *recipient* bacteria that differ from the donor bacteria in one mutant gene, some of the recipient bacteria are transformed hereditarily into the donor type. Thus the normal donor gene must have entered the transformed recipient bacterium in the form of a donor DNA molecule and there displaced its homologous mutant gene. Hence it followed that the material basis of the bacterial genes must be the bacterial DNA, or that DNA is *the* hereditary material. In 1944, this conclusion seemed so radical that even Avery himself was reluctant to accept it until he had buttressed his experiments with the most rigorous controls. Avery was not only not a member of the Phage Group—his laboratory had begun work on bacterial transformation more than a decade earlier—but his discovery also made, on first sight, a surprisingly small impact on the very people who had dedicated themselves to solving the problem of the physical basis of the gene. Indeed, as late as 1951, the finding of intracellular precursors of the viral protein at early stages of the latent period of phage-infected bacteria and the failure to find any identifiable precursors of the viral DNA at that same stage led, not unreasonably, to the hypothesis that the viral *protein* rather then the viral DNA is the genetic material of the virus. Finally, in 1952, Hershey and Martha Chase found that, in consonance with Avery's then eight-year-old demonstration, that the opposite is actually true. Hershey and Chase showed that at the outset of the bacteriophage infection of the *E. coli* cell only the DNA of the virus actually enters the cell, while the protein of the virus remains outside, devoid of any further function in the reproductive drama about to ensue within. Thus it could be concluded that the genes of the virus reside in the viral DNA. This second demonstration, originating within the Phage Group, that DNA is the hereditary material made a very profound impact on genetic thought.

On second sight, it is not all that surprising that Avery's identification of DNA as the hereditary material governing certain bacterial traits made a smaller impact on genetic thought in its day than the Hershey-Chase experiment made eight years later. First, it was only during the late 1940s that there emerged a general picture of bacteria as genetic organisms. Second, and more importantly, the notions extant in 1944 concerning the chemical structure of DNA made it very difficult to imagine how that molecule *could* be the carrier of hereditary information. It was then generally believed that the four types of nucleotides containing the nitrogenous bases adenine, thymine, guanine, and cytosine follow each other in regular alternation in the polynucleotide chain, and hence that DNA is a *monotonous* molecule. By 1951, however, the work of nucleic acid chemists, among them E. Chargaff, had shown that this earlier view was incorrect and that the four types of nucleotides could probably follow each other in any arbitrary order in the polynucleotide chain. Since that order was found to be different in DNA molecules obtained from different biological sources, it could now be supposed that any given DNA molecule harbors its genetic information in the form of a precise sequence of the four types of nucleotides along its polynucleotide chain. That is, Schrödinger's "aperiodic crystal" gene could now be identified with a polynucleotide chain, and the isomeric elements whose exact successions represent the hereditary code with the four types of nucleotides. In delaying for eight years its appreciation of Avery's discovery that the gene is DNA, the Phage Group had paid heed to the finding of physicist Arthur Eddington that "it is also a good rule not to put overmuch confidence in the observational results that are put forward until they have been confirmed by theory." This rule, which stands the principle of the inductive scientific method on its head, is often considered as a joke. But it is deadly serious and is a realistic description of the psychological dynamics that obtain at the frontier of scientific advance. Indeed, the thirty-five-year delay in the appreciation of the facts and inferences adduced by Mendel a century ago represents another example of Eddington's rule at work. For in 1865 there existed no way to connect Mendel's findings with the general conceptual framework of the then current views of the structure of cells and the physiology of reproduction. The deeper cognitive reasons underlying the operation of this rule will be of some importance in our later considerations of the future of science. We can already note here, however, that Eddington had divided scientists into two general archetypes, namely the "physicist" and the "stamp collector." To the former, observations are a bore unless he can infer some interesting connection between or among them, that is, unless he can perceive some meaningful structure, whereas for the latter an observation is an observation is an observation. Thus if, as I shall try to show later, progress in science beyond a certain point tends to make the perception of structure in an ensemble of observed events more and more difficult, "physicists" will quit the scene from boredom and leave the field to "stamp collectors."

The acceptance of DNA as the genetic material and the birth of the notion that the genetic information is encoded into it as a specific permutation of the four types of nucleotides, ushered in the end of the romantic period, since these insights presaged ominously that in the study of the genetic material no paradoxes might crop up and come into focus after all. For the fundamental problem of self-reproduction could now be restated in terms of two functions, "autocatalytic" and "heterocatalytic," of the phage DNA. By means of the former, the phage DNA replicates its precise nucleotide sequences a hundredfold to generate the genes of its progeny, and by means of the latter, the phage DNA induces, or presides over, the synthesis of the virus-specific proteins that furnish the body of its progeny.

Looking back now on the romantic period, a curious fact emerges: Though the experiments of that period and the immediate conclusions drawn from their results were almost always right, the more general and really interesting speculations built upon these first-order conclusions were generally mostly wrong. The outstanding accomplishment of the romantic period was therefore not so much the deep insights it provided but rather the introduction of previously unknown standards of experimental design, deductive logic, and data evaluation into the study of the genetics of bacteria and their viruses. For as it turned out, removal of the gene from its "classical" frame of reference of the indivisible, formal, and abstract unit and any experimental approach to its fine structure required the systematic study of events so rare and the manipulation of numbers of individuals so large that only organisms as tiny and as prolific as bacteria and their viruses could conveniently serve as experimental material. Furthermore, despite its frequently mistaken theories, the romantic period had provided the ideological basis for a sustained and concerted effort on the central problem of genetics that was to find its solution in the next decade.

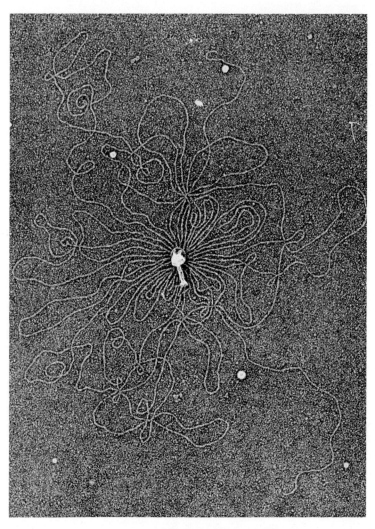

The DNA molecule of a bacteriophage, liberated from the virus head by osmotic shock. *Center:* the phage "ghost"; *bottom right and top center:* the two ends of the DNA molecule. (From Kleinschmidt, Lang, Jacherts, and Zahn, *Biochimica et Biophysica Acta,* Volume 61 [1962].)

3. THE DOGMATIC PERIOD

Concurrent with the rise of the Phage Group during the romantic period, there had also taken place a movement into biology of an entirely different group of physical scientists. In contrast to the Phage Group, whose efforts were motivated by the desire to understand the physical basis of the hereditary storage of biological information, the interest of these other men was focused on the three-dimensional structure, that is on the *form*, of biological molecules. This group of structural analysts, among whose preoccupations genetics played an at most peripheral role, can be considered as having descended from W. H. Bragg and W. L. Bragg. The Braggs, father and son, had invented X-ray crystallography in 1912. This invention engendered their founding a school of crystallographers that made Britain the home of molecular structure. As success came to the determination of the structures of ever more complicated molecules, these crystallographers became sufficiently emboldened to train their structural methods also on some very complex molecules of biological importance. For they had embraced the idea that the physiological function of the cell cannot be understood in terms other than of the spatial conformation of its elements. Among the first of the Bragg pupils to engage in this line of work were W. T. Astbury and J. D. Bernal, who in the late 1930s began to tackle the structural analysis of proteins and nucleic acids, that is of molecules containing thousands of atoms, and of aggregates at an even higher level of organization, such as viruses. The early stages of this movement, its personalities and milieu, are said to have provided the raw material for C. P. Snow's first novel, *The Search*.

To designate his approach to the understanding of life processes, Astbury coined the term *molecular biology*. Though for the next decade Astbury made vigorous propaganda in its favor, this neologism was very slow to find wide acceptance. Throughout the romantic period, for instance, no member of the Phage Group thought of or referred to himself as a "molecular biologist," for the very good reason that structure then played as peripheral a role in his preoccupations as did genetics in the preoccupations of the structural analysts. In fact, the Phage Group had *no* generic designation at all to describe its activity. Its members were most reluctant to call themselves, as might have seemed natural, "biophysicists." For, as was explicit in my earlier quotation from Delbrück's 1949 speech, "A Physicist Looks at Biology," they considered *that* term to have been "ill-used." More precisely, in the eyes of the Phage Group, two kinds of people were then wont to refer to themselves as "biophysicists": physiologists who were able to repair their own electronic equipment, and second-rate physicists who sought to convince biologists that they were first-rate. It was only in the wake of the confluence of structure and genetic analysis produced by the developments now to be recounted that the veterans of the romantic period and their disciples suddenly realized, like Monsieur Jourdain, that what they had been doing all along was molecular biology. Their pressing need for adopting *some* satisfactory cognomen for their line of work was later explained by Francis Crick: "I myself was forced to call myself a molecular biologist because when inquiring clergymen asked me what I did, I got tired of explaining that I was a mixture of crystallographer, biophysicist, biochemist and geneticist, an explanation which in any case they found too hard to grasp."

The early work of Astbury, Bernal, and other members of the British or structural school of molecular biology was to provide the foundation for the later and greater insights. However, the first great triumph of structural molecular biology was achieved not by a member of the British school, but by a Californian, Linus Pauling, who in 1951 discovered the basic structure of the protein molecule.

The twenty common amino acids found in proteins

Glycine (gly)

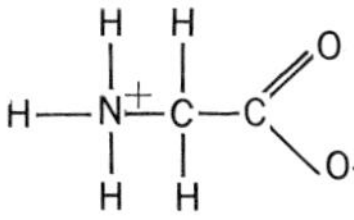

L-Alanine (ala)

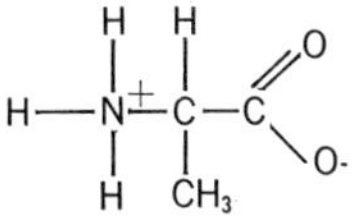

L-Valine (val)

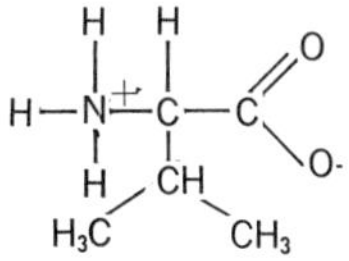

L-Isoleucine (ile)

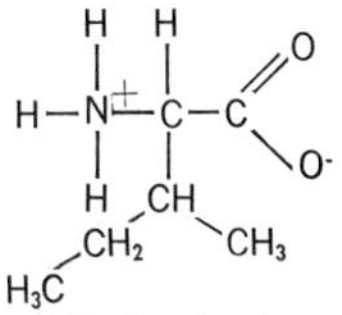

L-Leucine (leu)

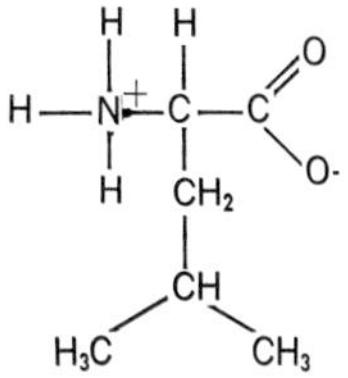

L-Serine (ser)

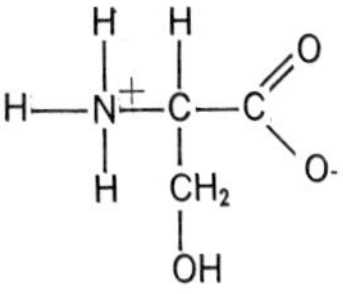

L-Threonine (thr)

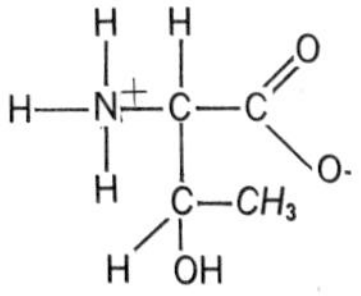

L-Proline (pro)

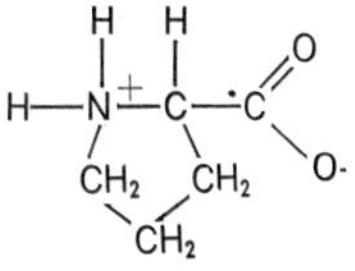

L-Aspartic acid (asp)

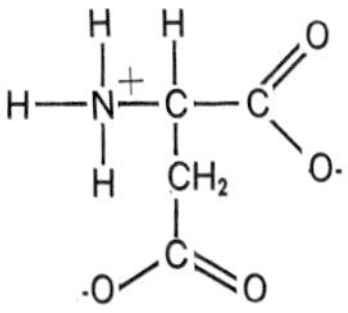

L-Glutamic acid (glu)

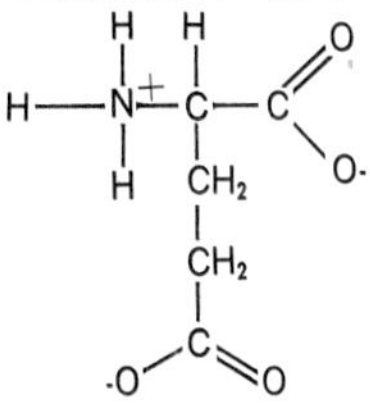

L-Lysine (lys)

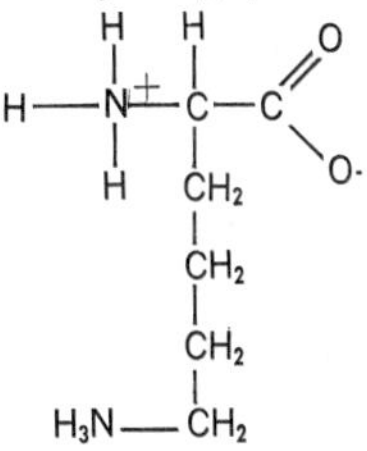

L-Arginine (arg)

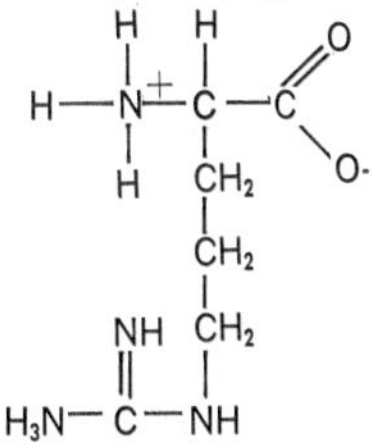

L-Asparagine (asn)

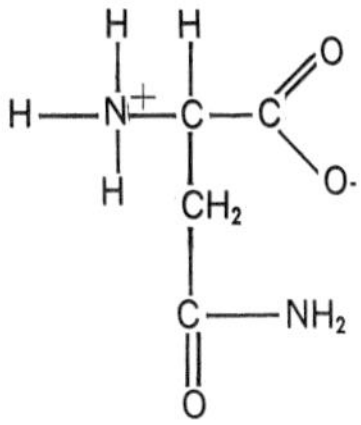

L-Glutamine (gln)

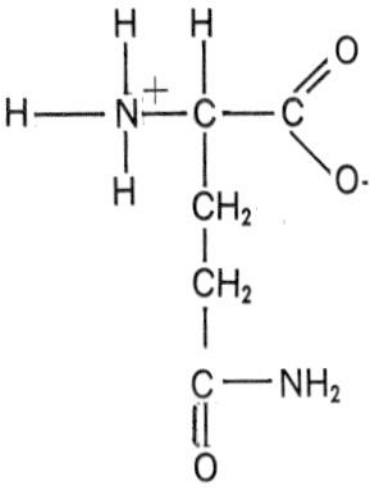

L-Cysteine (cys)

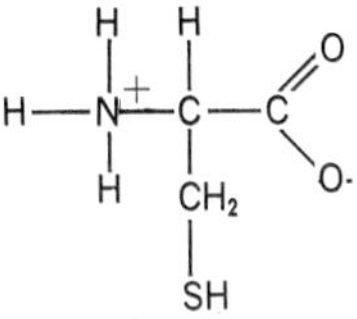

L-Methionine (met)

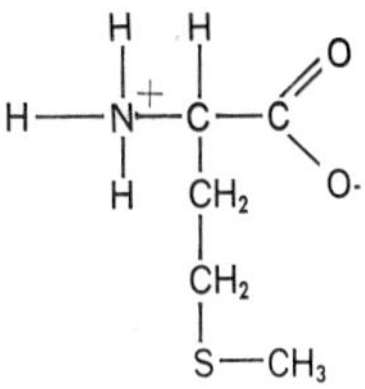

L-Tryptophan (try)

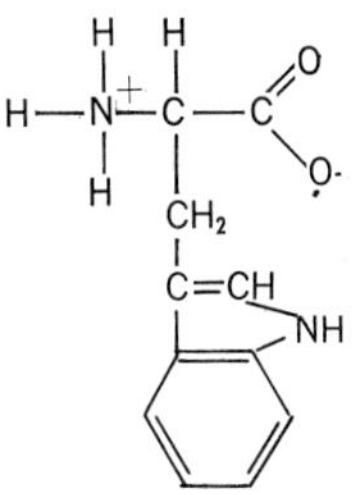

L-Phenylalanine (phe)

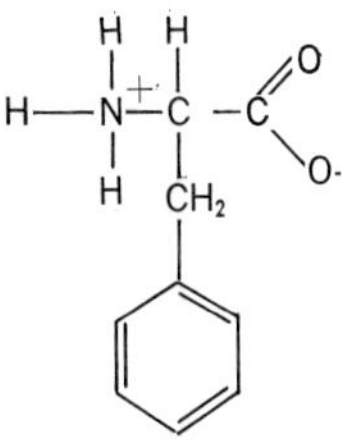

L-Tyrosine (tyr)

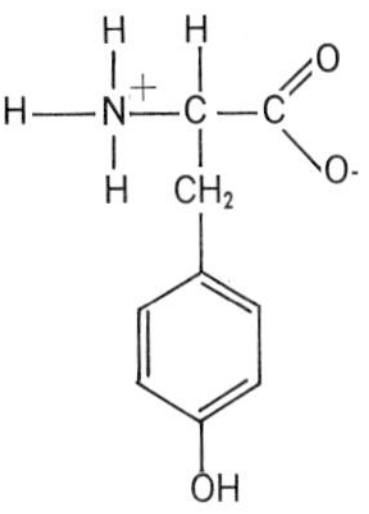

L-Histidine (his)

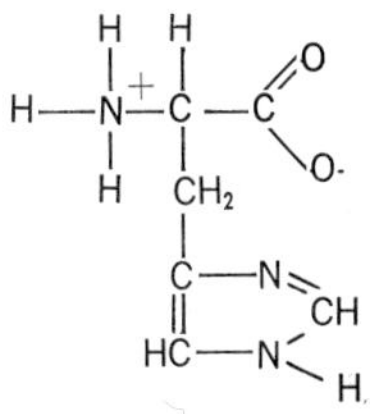

Proteins, we might recall here briefly, are composed of long-chain molecules, built up of a sequence of twenty different kinds of amino acids. These amino acids are joined to each other through a chemical linkage called the *peptide bond*, such an amino acid chain being called a *polypeptide*. The length of different kinds of polypeptide chains present in living cells varies considerably, but on the average these chains contain about three hundred amino acids linked end-to-end. Pauling had set himself the task of determining the spatial conformation of the polypeptide chain, that is, the shape of the backbone of the large protein molecule. He found that only a relatively limited number of helical shapes are possible for the backbone, and one of these, called the α-helix, was predicted to play a dominating role in determining the shapes of protein molecules—a prediction that was not long in being confirmed. Pauling's success was due in part to a novel approach to structure determination, in which guesswork and model building played a much greater role than in the more straightforward, analytical procedure of more conventional crystallographers. Pauling had decided some years earlier that it ought to be possible to deduce the structure of the polypeptide chain from a knowledge of the exact spatial arrangement of the peptide bond. He had, therefore, concentrated his X-ray crystallographic analyses on the structural determination of these bonds in simpler molecules. And once the exact structural details of these linkages were at his disposal, Pauling worked out the α-helix from first principles. Great triumph that it was, the discovery of the α-helix did not, however, immediately suggest to anyone very many new ideas about proteins, how they work, or how they are made. It did not seem to suggest many experiments, or to open new vistas to the imagination, except to show how very far one could go by use of the methods of structural analysis that Pauling had employed.

Meanwhile, in W. L. Bragg's laboratory in Cambridge, Max Perutz and John C. Kendrew had been working on the structures of the two respiratory proteins, hemoglobin and myoglobin. Their progress had been rather slow, since in view of the

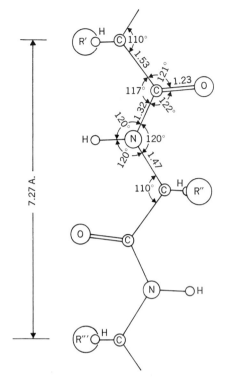

Structure of the peptide bond. Two peptide bonds are shown here, connecting three amino acids whose side chains are represented by circles labeled R', R", and R"'.

rather limited tools available at that time the task they had cut out for themselves was immensely difficult and complex. Pauling's brilliant success is said to have come as a bit of a shock to the Cambridge molecular biologists, but nevertheless they continued on undeterred. The application of the new analytical techniques to protein structure determination and the availability of ever more potent computers for the mathematical analysis of the X-ray photographs presently allowed Perutz and Kendrew to work out the complete three-dimensional structure of their respective proteins after nearly another ten years' labor. These structures included not only the conformation of the

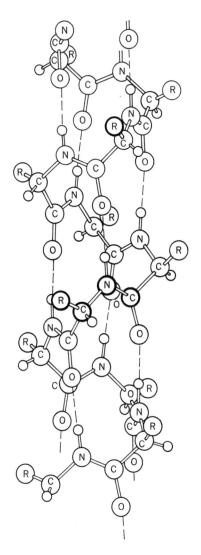

The Pauling α-helix structure of proteins. This drawing shows the three-dimensional conformation of a polypeptide chain of eleven amino acids, whose side chains are represented by circles labeled R. Hydrogen bonds are shown as dashed lines.

polypeptide backbone, which turned out to be only partly in the form of Pauling's α-helix, but also the position of every one of the thousands of atoms in these two giant molecules.

Pauling's success in 1951 in working out the basic structure of the protein molecule inspired James Watson, a then very young member of the Phage Group and a pupil of Luria, to abandon the genetic and physiological experiments on the reproduction of bacterial viruses he had been carrying out. Watson now decided to try to work out the basic structure of the DNA molecule, which the Hershey-Chase experiment had then recently shown to be the carrier of genetic information of the bacterial virus particle. To gain the necessary skills in X-ray crystallography, Watson joined Kendrew in Bragg's laboratory in Cambridge. There Watson met Francis Crick, to whom it had also occurred that knowing the three-dimensional structure of DNA would be likely to provide important insights into the nature of the gene. Watson and Crick then began a collaboration, which, in the spring of 1953, resulted in their discovery that the DNA molecule is a double helix, composed of two intertwined polynucleotide chains. The DNA double helix is self-complementary, in that to each adenine nucleotide on one chain there corresponds a thymine nucleotide on the other, and that to each guanine nucleotide on one chain there corresponds a cytosine nucleotide on the other. The specificity of this complementary relation devolves from hydrogen bonds formed between the two opposite nucleotides, adenine-thymine and guanine-cytosine, at each step of the double helical molecule.

On first sight, Watson and Crick's discovery of the double helical, self-complementary structure of DNA resembled Pauling's then two-year-old discovery of the α-helix, particularly since the formation of specific hydrogen bonds also plays an important role in Pauling's structure. But, on second sight, the promulgation of the DNA double helix emerges as an event of a qualitatively different heuristic nature. First, in working out the structure of the double helix, Watson and Crick had for the first time introduced genetic reasoning into structural determination by demanding that the evidently highly regular structure

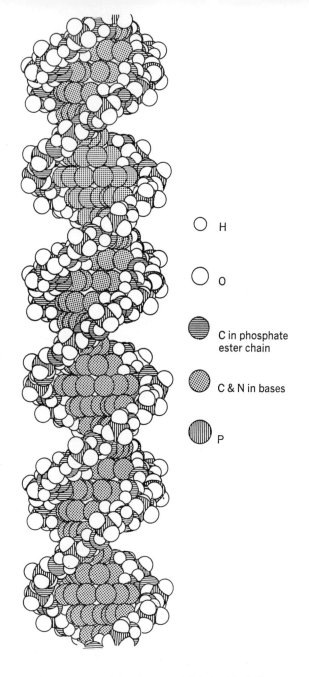

○	H
○	O
(shaded)	C in phosphate ester chain
(dotted)	C & N in bases
(striped)	P

A space-filling model of the Watson-Crick double helix structure of DNA. (From G. S. Stent, *Molecular Biology of Bacterial Viruses*, W. H. Freeman & Company, San Francisco, © 1963.)

of DNA must be able to accommodate the informational element of arbitrary nucleotide base sequence along the two polynucleotide strands. Second, unlike the discovery of the protein α-helix, the discovery of the DNA double helix opened up enormous vistas to the imagination. It was to provide the highroad to understanding how the genetic material functions.

This brilliant wedding of structural and genetic considerations embodied in the DNA helix engendered the next phase in the study of genetics, the *dogmatic period*, which lasted from 1953 until about 1963. By the end of that decade, the number of working molecular geneticists had to be reckoned in the hundreds, rather than in the dozens as at the end of the romantic period. But two men can, nevertheless, be clearly identified as having dominated the dogmatic period: Watson and Crick. For they were in the main responsible for formulating the *central dogma* of molecular genetics that was now to guide most of the research on the nature of the gene. It is the existence of the central dogma that sharply distinguished the Zeitgeist of the dogmatic from that of the romantic period. For whereas the romantic period involved groping for the still unimaginable, test and elaboration of the clearly stated central dogma characterized the dogmatic period. The only hope now left for the veterans of the romantic period of encountering a paradox during the dogmatic period was that the central dogma might somehow prove to be untrue.

The central dogma represents a series of beliefs which give a coherent account of the mechanisms by means of which the DNA achieves the two fundamental functions that had come into focus at the end of the romantic period: the "autocatalytic" and the "heterocatalytic" functions. In its most abbreviated form, the dogma states that the autocatalytic function is a one-stage process, in which the DNA molecule serves directly as a template for the synthesis of its own DNA replica polynucleotide chain. The heterocatalytic function, however, is a two-stage process, in which the second type of nucleic acid, RNA, becomes involved. In the first stage, the DNA molecule serves as a template for the synthesis of an RNA polynucleotide chain onto

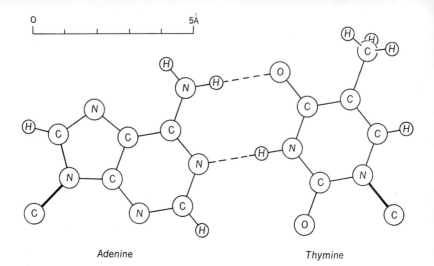

Adenine   Thymine

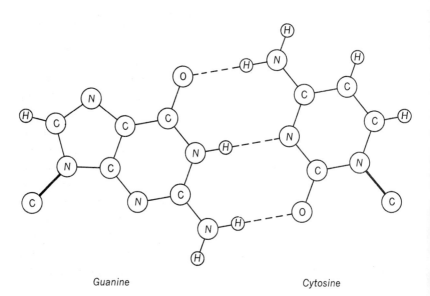

Guanine   Cytosine

The complementary base pairing of adenine and thymine, and of guanine and cytosine in the double-helical DNA molecule. Hydrogen bonds are shown as dashed lines. The carbon atom of the deoxyribose to which each base is attached is also shown. (From G. S. Stent, *Molecular Biology of Bacterial Viruses*, W. H. Freeman & Company, San Francisco, © 1963.)

which the sequence of nucleotides in the DNA chain is *transcribed*. In the second stage, the RNA chain is then *translated* by the cellular machinery for protein synthesis into polypeptide chains of the required structure. It is to be noted that an essential feature of the central dogma is a one-way flow of information from DNA to RNA to protein, a flow the direction of which is never reversed.

This view of the heterocatalytic function of DNA was predicated on an ancillary dogma, for which there was no proof whatever at the time it was embraced. This ancillary dogma, or "sequence hypothesis," states that the exact spatial conformation of a protein molecule, and hence the specificity of its biological function, is wholly determined by the particular sequence of the twenty kinds of amino acids which make up its polypeptide chains. Hence, the "meaning" of the particular sequence of the four types of nucleotides making up a sector of DNA corresponding to a gene could be nothing other than the specification of an amino acid sequence of some polypeptide chain.

As far as the autocatalytic function was concerned, Watson and Crick proposed that the parental DNA molecule achieves its replication upon separation of the two helically intertwined, complementary polynucleotide strands. Each of the two parent strands then serves as a template for the ordered synthesis of its own complementary daughter strand, by having each nucleotide on the parent strand attract and line up for polynucleotide synthesis the complementary free nucleotide. Thus in the case of bacteriophage reproduction—leitmotiv of the romantic period —the DNA of the infecting parental virus would undergo successive rounds of unwinding and complement addition. In this way an intrabacterial pool of replica viral DNA molecules identical in nucleotide sequence to the DNA of the parent virus would be built up; this pool provides the genes for the offspring virus. From the purview of the central dogma, gene mutations then represent rare errors in this template-copy process, by means of which changes in the parental DNA nucleotide sequence arise. These changes evidently cause an alteration of the hereditary information encoded into the particular gene

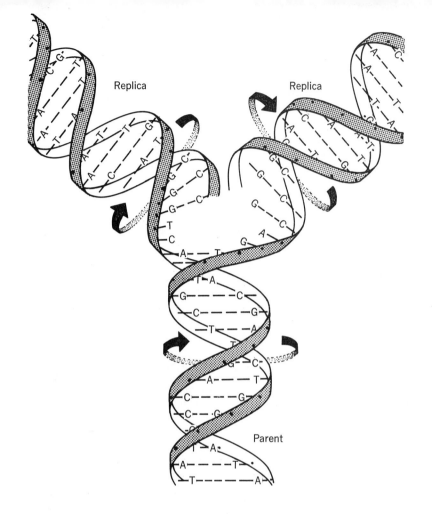

Replica

Replica

Parent

Replication of the DNA double helix, according to the mechanism of Watson and Crick. (From G. S. Stent, *Molecular Biology of Bacterial Viruses*, W. H. Freeman & Company, San Francisco, © 1963.)

represented by the stretch of DNA in which the copy error had occurred. It took about five years to prove that this view of the autocatalytic function is essentially correct. The main proof consisted of the demonstration in 1958 that in the replication of the DNA molecules the atoms of the parental double helix are distributed in a *semi-conservative* manner. That is, as demanded by the proposal of Watson and Crick, each replica DNA mole-

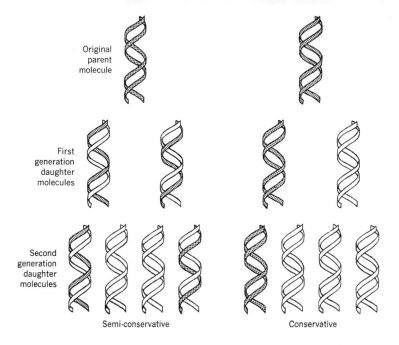

Original parent molecule

First generation daughter molecules

Second generation daughter molecules

Semi-conservative   Conservative

Semi-conservative and conservative distribution of the two parental polynucleotide chains as possible alternatives in the replication of DNA. (From G. S. Stent, *Molecular Biology of Bacterial Viruses*, W. H. Freeman & Company, San Francisco, © 1963.)

cule contains one polynucleotide chain of parental provenance and one chain synthesized *de novo*.

Detailed understanding of the heterocatalytic function, which from the very outset of its formulation appeared to be a more complex problem than the autocatalytic function, required a rather greater effort and a somewhat longer time. First of all, it proved necessary to reform the concept of the gene itself, which, within the frame of reference of classical genetics, had been the fundamental hereditary unit of function, mutation, and crossing over. This reform was carried out by Seymour Benzer, who made a *fine-structure* study of a single gene of the bacteriophage. In the course of this work, Benzer examined the genetically hybrid virus offspring arising from a mixed infection of one bacterium with two genetically different parent viruses. The novelty of Benzer's approach was that the two parent viruses he employed carried different mutations in the *same* gene. He searched among the phage progeny of this genetic cross for *non-mutant* recombinant viruses, that is, for viruses whose DNA nucleotide sequence had arisen as the result of a crossover *within* the gene in question. For if there occurs a crossover *between* the two mutational sites, two new types of progeny viruses must arise: one type which is a double mutant, in that it has drawn both of the two different mutations of its two parents, and one type which is nonmutant, in that it has drawn neither of the two parental mutations. Since crossovers between two very closely linked genetic sites are very improbable, recombinants of the type Benzer was hoping to find are very rare. But the techniques of bacteriophage genetics allowed Benzer to find his recombinants, even though they appeared as rarely as one phage in a million, a feat that would have been a technical impossibility using the fruit fly Drosophila as the experimental material. In this way Benzer showed that there really is no such thing as the classical gene, a unit which is at the same time a unit of function, mutation, and crossing over. The unit of crossing over is the single nucleotide in the DNA molecule; that is, two genetic sites can be separated in a crossover event if they represent adjacent nucleotides in the two parental polynucleotide chains. The unit of mutation ranges from the single nucleotide (in the case of "point" mutations) to hundreds or thousands of nucleotides (in the case of "deletion" mutations). And the unit of function is of the order of a thousand nucleotides. Benzer gave the name "cistron" to the unit of function, which corresponds to that stretch of a DNA molecule in which the sequence of animo acids of a particular polypeptide chain is encoded as a particular sequence of the four kinds of nucleotides. The "one gene-one enzyme" theory, whose promulgation by Beadle and Tatum had coincided with the opening phase of the romantic period, now reappeared in modern dress as the "one cistron-one polypeptide" dogma.

The central dogma and its ancillary "sequence hypothesis" had led directly to the belief that there must exist a *genetic code* that relates the nucleotide sequence in the DNA polynucleotide chain to amino acid sequence in the corresponding polypeptide chain. A simple consideration quickly revealed that this code could be no simpler than one involving the specification of each amino acid in the polypeptide chain by at least three successive nucleotides in the DNA. That is, four kinds of nucleotides taken three at a time provide $4 \times 4 \times 4 = 64$ different code words, or *codons*. Each of the twenty kinds of protein amino acids could then be represented by at least one such codon in the genetic code, though the greater number of available kinds of codons than of kinds of amino acids would allow also for the possibility that the code provides for the representation of one kind of amino acid by more than a single codon. These *a priori* insights into the nature of the genetic code had been reached soon after the onset of the dogmatic period and were first committed to print in 1954 by the physicist-cosmologist George Gamow. But it was not until 1961 that it was finally proved that the genetic code really does involve a language in which successive nucleotides in the DNA polynucleotide chain are read three-by-three in the polypeptide translation process. That proof came from purely formal genetic experiments carried out by Crick and his collaborators with the same bacteriophage cistron which had figured in Benzer's earlier reform of the gene concept. As we shall see presently, the code was unexpectedly broken in that same year.

It was all well and good to have demonstrated the formal, informational principles of the heterocatalytic function. But in order to really understand its molecular processes, it became necessary to employ the methods of biochemistry to open the black box containing the cellular hardware which actually effects the transcription-translation drama of the central dogma. One of the first insights then provided by the application of biochemical methods was the identification of the *ribosome* as the *site* of cellular protein synthesis. The ribosome is a small particle present in vast numbers in all living cells (one *E. coli* bacterium contains about fifteen thousand ribosomes). The mass of the ribosome is composed of about one-third protein and two-thirds RNA. But how is the information for specific amino acid permutations encoded in the cistron made available to the ribosome in its polypeptide assembly process? In answer to this question it was proposed in 1961 by François Jacob and Jacques Monod that the RNA onto which, according to the central dogma, the cistronic nucleotide sequence is first transcribed, is a molecule of *messenger RNA*. This messenger RNA molecule is picked up by a ribosome, on whose surface then proceeds the translation of RNA nucleotide sequence into polypeptide amino acid sequence, codon by codon. In this translation process, the messenger RNA chains runs through the ribosome like a tape runs through a tape recorder head. While the tail of a messenger RNA molecule is still running through one ribosome, its head may already have been picked up by another ribosome, so that a single molecule of messenger RNA can actually service several ribosomes at the same time. How the amino acids are actually assembled into the correct predetermined permutation by the messenger RNA as it runs through the ribosome had been envisaged by Crick in about 1958, before the concept of the messenger RNA had even been clearly formulated. Crick thought it unlikely, again, as was his wont, from first principles, that the twenty different amino acids could interact in any specific way directly with the nucleotide triplet on the RNA template chain. He therefore proposed the idea of a nucleotide *adaptor*, with which each amino acid is outfitted prior to its incorporation into the polypeptide chain. This adaptor was thought to contain a nucleotide triplet, or *anticodon*, complementary (in the Watson-Crick nucleotide pairing sense) to the nucleotide triplet codon that codes for the particular amino acid to which the adaptor is attached. The anticodon nucleotides of the adaptor would then form specific hydrogen bonds with their complementary codon nucleotides on the messenger RNA and thus bring the amino acids bearing the adaptor into the proper, predetermined alignment on the ribosome surface. No sooner had the adaptor hypothesis been formulated than students of the biochemistry of protein synthesis began to encounter an ensemble of specific reactions and enzymes that gradually resembled more and more the *a priori* postulates of that hypothesis. First, a special type of small RNA molecule, the *transfer RNA*, was discovered, which contains about eighty nucleotides in its polynucleotide chain.

Each cell contains several dozen distinct species of transfer RNA, each species being capable of combining with one and only one kind of amino acid. This transfer RNA turned out to be Crick's postulated adaptor, since that transfer RNA species which accepts any given amino acid contains the anticodon nucleotide triplet in its polynucleotide chain which is complementary to the codon representing that same amino acid in the genetic code. Second, a set a enzymes, the *amino acid activating enzymes*, was discovered, each of whose members is capable of catalyzing the combination of one kind of amino acid with its cognate transfer RNA molecule. Thus the set of activating enzymes which matches each amino acid with its proper transfer RNA adaptor (by means of which the amino acid is recognized in polypeptide formation) evidently represents the *dictionary of heredity*, the cellular agency that "knows" the genetic code.

The actual deciphering, or breaking of the genetic code began with a discovery made by the then virtually unknown young biochemist Marshall Nirenberg. In the spring of 1961, Nirenberg had managed to develop a "cell-free" system capable of linking amino acid into polypeptides. This system contained ribosomes, transfer RNA, and amino acid activating enzymes extracted from *E. coli*. Though Nirenberg was by no means the first to reassemble *in vitro* the cellular components for protein formation, his system had one very important advantage over its predecessors: Here polypeptide synthesis depended on the addition of messenger RNA to the reaction mixture. Thus it became feasible to direct the *in vitro* formation of specific polypeptides by introducing into this system arbitrary types of messenger RNA. Now when Nirenberg introduced a synthetically produced *monotonous* RNA containing *only* the uracil nucleotide (instead of the four types of nucleotides present in natural messenger RNA), he obtained a dramatic result. Addition of the artificial, monotonous messenger RNA resulted in the *in vitro* formation of an equally monotonous polypeptide, namely a polypeptide containing only one kind of amino acid: phenylalanine. This result could have only one meaning: In the genetic code the uracil-uracil-uracil nucleotide triplet represents the amino acid phenyl-

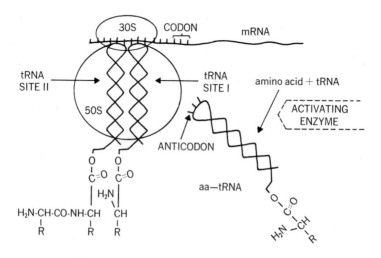

REPLICATION   TRANSCRIPTION   TRANSLATION

DNA   mRNA   POLYSOME
Polarity →   70S
30S   50S
70S   NASCENT   FINISHED

30S   CODON   mRNA
tRNA SITE II   tRNA SITE I   amino acid + tRNA
50S   ACTIVATING ENZYME
ANTICODON   aa—tRNA
H_2N-CH-CO-NH-CH   CH

alanine. Nirenberg announced his identification of the first codon in August of 1961, at the International Congress of Biochemistry in Moscow, where it caused a sensation. (Crick later wrote that he was "electrified.") Thus at one stroke the breaking of the genetic code had become accessible to direct chemical experimentation, because now the effect of introducing various synthetically produced types of messenger RNA of known composition into the cell-free protein synthesizing system could be examined. The Moscow announcement set off a code-breaking race, sometimes called the Code War of the U_3 Incident, which culminated in deciphering the definite, or at least probable meaning of many of the sixty-four codons by 1963.

The developments recounted so far had revealed the *qualita-*

A summary diagram of the autocatalytic (replication) and hetero-catalytic (transcription and translation) functions of DNA. *Upper left:* The DNA double helix replicates according to the semi-con-servative Watson-Crick mechanism. *Upper center:* The DNA nucle-otide sequence has been transcribed onto a molecule of messenger, or mRNA. The mRNA molecule is engaged by ribosomes, which are composed of two subunits, a smaller one called 30S and a larger one called 50S. The two subunits together constitute the intact, or 70S ribosome. *Upper right:* Each of several ribosomes working in tandem on the same mRNA molecule (a "polysome") translates the mRNA nucleotide sequence into the corresponding polypeptide chain. When a ribosome has translated the entire nucleotide sequence corresponding to a gene, the completed polypeptide chain is released, and the ribosome is free to attach itself to another mRNA molecule. *Lower part:* Details of the process of polypeptide assembly. The nascent polypeptide chain (here consisting merely of two amino acid residues) is attached to that molecule of transfer, or tRNA which figured as adaptor of the last amino acid to be added into the chain. This molecule of tRNA is in turn held to site II of the 50S ribosomal subunit. The next amino acid to be incorporated into the nascent polypeptide chain is specified by that nucleotide triplet codon of the mRNA which faces site I of the 50S subunit. Into site I can fit only a molecule of tRNA whose anticodon matches the codon displayed by the mRNA and to which the appropriate amino acid has become attached, thanks to the recognition effected by the activating enzyme. Once the tRNA has entered site I, its amino acid has been brought into juxtaposition with the last amino acid of the nascent polypeptide chain, and the next peptide bond can be formed. When the chain has thus been elongated by one amino acid residue, mRNA and tRNA molecules move over the ribosome from right to left, so as to trans-locate the tRNA now carrying the nascent chain from site I to site II and to display the next codon at site I. (From H. K. Das, A. Gold-stein, and L. C. Kanner, *Molecular Pharmacology*, Vol. 2, 158–70 [1966].)

tive aspect of the heterocatalytic function, namely how the nu-cleotide sequence carried by the DNA is finally translated into the predetermined amino acid sequence. However, there must pertain to the heterocatalytic function also a *quantitative* aspect, namely how the DNA manages to govern the synthesis of appro-priate amounts of the different polypeptides encoded into it. For it is an easily ascertainable fact that in *E. coli* the number of polypeptide chains read from one cistron per generation time can exceed by more than ten-thousandfold the corresponding number read from another cistron in the same cell. Furthermore, the rate of translation of any given cistron is not always the same, being very high under some conditions and very low un-der other conditions. The framework for understanding this quantitative aspect, which was not really covered by the original formulation of the central dogma, was finally provided in 1961 by the *operon theory* of Jacob and Monod. In order to explain the functional regulation of the cistrons of *E. coli* and its bacteriophage, this theory envisages that a group of cistrons, or an *operon*, is subject to coordinate control. The cistrons belonging to the same operon occupy contiguous sectors of the DNA, i.e., are closely linked, and share a common, special regulatory segment of DNA, their *operator*. This operator, which is located at one extreme of the operon group of cistrons, can exist in two states: open or closed. As long as the operator is open, messenger RNA can be transcribed from all the cistrons of the operon, and hence synthesis of the polypeptide chains encoded into these cistrons may proceed on the ribosomes into which these messenger RNA molecules are fed. As soon as the operator is closed, transcription of the messenger RNA stops, and hence synthesis of the encoded polypeptide chains ceases. Thus the rate of translation of the cistrons belonging to any operon depends on the fraction of the time during which their operator happens to be open. Now whether the operator is open or closed in turn de-

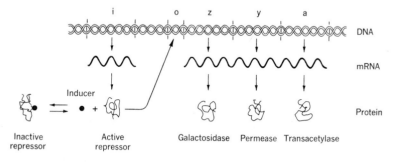

The operon theory of Jacob and Monod, as applied to the lactose fermentation genes of *E. coli*. Three contiguous genes, *z*, *y*, and *a*, code for the protein structure of three enzymes, galactosidase, permease, and transacetylase, and share a common operator gene, *o*. A nearby gene, *i*, codes for the protein structure of the repressor, which can attach to, and thus "close," gene *o*. Combination with an inducer, such as lactose, inactivates the repressor, thus preventing it from "closing" *o*. (From G. S. Stent, in *The Neurosciences*, Rockefeller University Press, New York [1967].)

pends on whether it has interacted with a *repressor* polypeptide, itself the product of a special regulatory cistron. Combination of the operator segment with the repressor affined to it inhibits transcription of the cistrons of that operon, and therefore closes the operator. Hence, in the last analysis, the rate of translation of any cistron is a function of the intracellular concentration of active repressor capable of combining with the operator segment of DNA to which that cistron is linked.

Thus, by about 1963 the general nature of both autocatalytic and heterocatalytic functions of DNA were understood. Through formation of complementary hydrogen bonds, DNA achieves both functions by serving as a template for the synthesis of replica polynucleotide chains, making DNA chains for the autocatalytic function and RNA chains for the heterocatalytic function. RNA, in turn, completes the heterocatalytic function by formation of complementary hydrogen bonds with the anticodons of the transfer RNA molecules in the amino acid assembly processes. The central dogma turned out to be essentially correct. Bohr's expectation that the necessity for keeping alive an organism under study would hide its ultimate secrets from us did not prove to be a barrier to fathoming the nature of the gene. (However, there might be thought to exist some kind of "uncertainty principle" of heredity, in that it is probably impossible in principle to specify with absolute accuracy the total nucleotide sequence of the DNA of any given single cell.) And just as Delbrück had thought, the long-term stability of the genetic information *is* maintained in the face of metabolic reactions in the cell by having each atom of the gene molecule fixed in its mean position and electronic state. That is, the genetic atoms form part of the chemically covalent continuum of the polynucleotide chain. Or, Schrödinger's vision of the chromosome as an "aperiodic crystal" materialized into the form of the Watson-Crick double helix. No deep paradoxes had come into focus, no "other laws" of physics had come into view. Formation of complementary hydrogen bonds seems to be all there is to the process by means of which like begets like.

Solemn Inauguration of the Academic Period; Stockholm 1962. Francis Crick receives the Nobel Prize from King Gustav VI, under the eyes of his fellow laureates (from left to right) Max Perutz, John Kendrew, Maurice Wilkins and James Watson. (Photograph provided by James Watson.)

4. THE ACADEMIC PERIOD

The realization of the essential truth of the central dogma and of its one great theoretical extension, the operon, now brought molecular genetics to the spiritual state which classical genetics had reached a quarter of a century earlier. The gene problem was solved; what remained now was to iron out the details. And so molecular genetics entered its last or *academic period*. Many important achievements were made in the five years for which this academic period has so far lasted, some of them by virtuosi of biochemical experimentation. Nevertheless, though at the outset of his career no veteran of the romantic period could have reasonably hoped to witness these recent developments during his own lifetime, the denouement of the central dogma has rendered it very difficult to find the events of the academic period very exciting. Success has dulled the sensibilities. Let us now consider briefly some of these latter-day achievements.

First of all, it had become clear that a very large fraction of the entire genetic material of the *E. coli* bacterium and of the bacterial viruses parasitic on it is now known. The inference that there could no longer exist a vast *terra incognita* of as yet unrecognized genes in these organisms follows from a simple calculation of their total content of genetic information. As far as one of these bacterial viruses is concerned, its entire DNA complement consists of two helically intertwined polynucleotide chains, each about 200,000 nucleotides in length. Thus, because of the triplet nature of the genetic code, this corresponds to the specification of a total polypeptide sequence of $\frac{200,000}{3} = 70,000$ amino acids. Now since the average polypeptide chain contains about 300 amino acids, the grand number of different polypeptide chains specified, and hence of cistrons, is of the order of $\dfrac{200,000}{3 \times 300} = 200$.

At the present time, about 100 cistrons, or half the estimated total, have been identified and ordered on the genetic map of the virus. As far as *E. coli* is concerned, whose DNA complement consists of twice 6,000,000 nucleotides, an analogous calculation leads to the rough-and-ready estimate of a total of 5000 cistrons. About a third of that number of cistrons is presently known on the bacterial genetic map. Naturally, some of the as yet unknown cistrons may still hold big surprises in store for us, but the possible number of such surprises is not likely to be very large.

The autocatalytic reaction of DNA, understood in principle since 1953, was worked out in greater detail. As early as the late 1950s, Arthur Kornberg had isolated an enzyme from *E. coli* which is capable of catalyzing the synthesis of DNA polynucleotides *in vitro*. In the following years, Kornberg and his colleagues adduced more and more evidence that this enzyme really does carry out a faithful *in vitro* replication of the DNA template provided to it in the reaction mixture. Indeed, the discovery of this enzyme had furnished the best proof of the truth of the first article of the central dogma, namely that the parental DNA molecule serves directly as the template for the synthesis of its own replica. In 1967, Kornberg finally succeeded in showing that his enzyme can actually copy the entire DNA complement of a bacteriophage so faithfully that the test-tube-synthesized, and hence man-made, replica DNA can infect a bacterium and give rise to live progeny virus particles. If any member of the Phage Group had said in 1947 that he believed such a thing could be done twenty years hence, he would have been thrown out of the club for being a fool. But last year this feat caused more excitement among the general public than among molecular geneticists, few of whom had any reason to doubt that genetically active DNA *would* be made sooner or later. In any case, a self-reproducing RNA polynucleotide had already been synthesized enzymatically by Sol Spiegelman two years earlier.

Some unexpected features of the DNA molecule did come to light during the academic period, however. For instance, nucleotide *repair* processes were discovered, which enormously increase the reliability of the DNA double helix as an information store. Thus if one nucleotide in one of the two complementary polynucleotide chains happens to have been damaged, for instance by irradiation, then a special enzyme can cut out the lesion. Afterward, the correct nucleotide sequence is restored to the damaged chain by means of a repair replication of the excised polynucleotide segment, using the undamaged segment of the complementary chain as a template. Neither Delbrück nor Schrödinger had suspected twenty-five years earlier this dynamic contribution to the stability of the gene as an information carrier, though the principle of self-repair by means of redundant components was meanwhile discovered independently in electronic computer design. Such excision and repair enzymes also appear to be involved in the molecular mechanism of the genetic crossing over of DNA molecules.

Throughout the dogmatic period, it had been assumed tacitly that the nucleotide sequence in the DNA segment representing a cistron is *colinear* with the amino acid sequence of the polypeptide which it specifies. That is, it was taken for granted that the first nucleotide triplet in the cistron specifies the first amino acid in the polypeptide, the second nucleotide triplet specifies the second amino acid, and so on. But for more than a decade, the only justification for believing in this assumption had been the success encountered by operating as if it *were* true. Finally, in 1966 by work whose level of technical rafinesse would have staggered the imagination in the romantic period, the colinearity of genetic nucleotide sequence and protein amino acid sequence was proven directly. But when this proof finally came, it seemed more cause for disappointment than for elation. So, the colinearity was true; how much more interesting it would have been had it turned out to be untrue after all! Similarly, it had long been assumed, as a necessary ancillary to the central dogma, that the form, or three-dimensional conformation, of a protein molecule, and hence the specificity of its physiological action, is wholly determined by the amino acid sequence of its polypeptide chain. This assumption too was to find its direct experimental vindication presently. Finally, it had been believed that the aggregation of different kinds of proteins into larger, more complex cellular structures is an automatic process, which will occur spontaneously once an ensemble of protein molecules of the requisite specific forms is brought together under appropriate environmental conditions. This belief had already received some support in 1956 when it was shown that the 2150 molecules of a single type of protein composing the shell of the tobacco mosaic virus can be made to assemble *in vitro* into the helically shaped virus rod *in vitro*. But in 1966 it was found that the much more complex ensemble of proteins making up the tail and head of the bacteriophage will also unite spontaneously in a specific reaction sequence to constitute the structurally intact, infective virus particle. Thus, complex morphogenetic reactions had finally become accessible to direct experimental study, and, in their turn, lost most of their possibilities for harboring paradoxes.

An important technical achievement of the academic period was the *in vitro* formation of double helical polynucleotide chains from single polynucleotide chains of complementary nucleotide sequence. In particular, it became possible to match single RNA chains with single DNA chains to form DNA-RNA *hybrid* molecules. In this way, the genetic provenance, and hence identity of a given set of messenger RNA molecules could be ascertained, by testing them against a set of DNA molecules and determining whether the nucleotide sequences of RNA and DNA polynucleotide chains are sufficiently complementary to form a hybrid double helix. For it follows from the central dogma that the nucleotide sequence of a messenger RNA molecule should be complementary to that of the DNA template chain from which it has been transcribed in the first stage of the heterocatalytic reaction. The first significant result obtained by means of the DNA-RNA hybridization reaction was the demonstration of the justice of an essential feature of Jacob and Monod's operon theory. According to that theory, the rate of cellular synthesis of a particular polypeptide encoded in a particular cistron is but a reflection of the rate of transcription, and hence of the rate of synthesis, of messenger RNA affined to that cistron. By measuring the intracellular amount of messenger RNA capable of forming a molecular hybrid with the DNA representing a given cistron, it was shown that, just as demanded by the operon theory, this amount increases with increases in the rate of synthesis of the polypeptide known to be encoded in that cistron. Proof of another essential feature of the operon theory came in 1967, when the postulated repressor polypeptide was finally isolated. Just as demanded by that theory, bacteria do contain a protein which combines with, and hence "closes," the regulatory operator segment of DNA. Thus there now remains little doubt that, for at least some genes, the quantitative aspect of the heterocatalytic function *is* regulated in the manner envisaged by Jacob and Monod.

In 1964, Nirenberg made a second experimental breakthrough in the deciphering of the genetic code by means of his "cell-free" system for protein synthesis. At that time, he discovered that it is possible to detect in the reaction mixture he devised the specific *binding* to ribosomes of molecules of transfer RNA carrying their cognate amino acids. In particular, he found that addition to his reaction mixture of a very short polynucleotide consisting of only three nucleotides, instead of messenger RNA, promotes the specific binding to ribosomes of those and only those transfer RNA molecules that carry the anticodon complementary in the Watson-Crick base-pairing sense to the nucleotide triplet added to the reaction mixture. Polypeptide formation does not, of course, occur under these conditions since the short nucleotide triplet cannot serve as the template for directing the assembly of many amino acids. By means of this new technique, Nirenberg found, in confirmation of his earlier identification of the codon representing the amino acid phenylalanine, that addition of the uracil-uracil-uracil nucleotide triplet promotes the binding of phenylalanine transfer RNA to ribosomes. And since it was relatively easy to prepare by chemical methods all sixty-four possible nucleotide triplets, the entire code could be worked out by use of this binding method within little more than a year. The result of this work, which was presently supported or confirmed by other methods, is now generally presented in the form of a table, the arrangement of which was conceived by Crick.

It has been suggested that this table of the code represents for biology what the periodic table of the elements represents for chemistry. The important features of the genetic code are these: (1) The code contains synonyms, in that many amino acids are represented by more than one kind of codon. Thus the nucleotide triplets uracil-uracil-uracil *and* uracil-uracil-cytosine are synonyms, in that they both code for phenylalanine. (2) The code has a definite structure, in that synonymous codons representing the same amino acid are nearly always in the same "box" of the table. That is, the synonymous codons generally differ from each other only in the third of their three nucleotides. An explanation for this aspect of the code was provided by Crick, in terms of the geometry of the hydrogen bonds involved in the recognition of the messenger RNA codon by the transfer RNA anticodon at the ribosomal site of polypeptide formation. (3) The code is very nearly universal. Though most of the code was deciphered by use of the protein-synthesizing machinery of *E. coli*, later tests showed that the results are very much the same whether the transfer RNA and amino acid activating enzymes (the agency that "knows" the code) are obtained from bacterial, plant, or animal sources (including mammals). The universality of the code among contemporary living forms shows that the code has remained unchanged over a very long period of organic evolution. One explanation which has been offered for the (at first sight surprising) evolutionary permanence of the code is that any genetic mutation engendering a change in the code, by means of which evolution of the code would have had to have proceeded, would necessarily be lethal to the organism in which it took place. For such a mutational alteration of the code would

THE GENETIC CODE

	U	C	A	G	
U	Phe	Ser	Tyr	Cys	U
	Phe	Ser	Tyr	Cys	C
	Leu	Ser	—	—	A
	Leu	Ser	—	Try	G
C	Leu	Pro	His	Arg	U
	Leu	Pro	His	Arg	C
	Leu	Pro	Gln	Arg	A
	Leu	Pro	Gln	Arg	G
A	Ile	Thr	Asn	Ser	U
	Ile	Thr	Asn	Ser	C
	Ile	Thr	Lys	Arg	A
	Met	Thr	Lys	Arg	G
G	Val	Ala	Asp	Gly	U
	Val	Ala	Asp	Gly	C
	Val	Ala	Glu	Gly	A
	Val	Ala	Glu	Gly	G

In this table, the letters U, C, A, and G represent the four kinds of nucleotides, containing respectively the bases uracil, cytosine, adenine, and guanine. The three-letter words represent the twenty kinds of protein amino acids, whose chemical structures are shown on page 37. The codon corresponding to any given position on this table can be read off according to the following rules: The base of the first nucleotide of the codon is given by the capital letter on the left, which defines a horizontal row containing four lines. The base of the second nucleotide is given by the capital letter on the top, which defines a vertical column containing sixteen codons. The intersection of rows and columns defines a "box" of four codons, all of which carry the same bases in their first and second nucleotides. The base of the third nucleotide is given by the capital letter on the right, which defines one line within any given horizontal row. The triplets UAA, UAG, and UGA are "nonsense" codons, to which there corresponds no amino acid.

cause a sudden, and presumably deleterious change in *all* of the protein molecules of the mutant organism. Another possible explanation for the evolutionary permanence of the code is that there exists some as yet unfathomed geometrical or stereochemical relation between the anticodon nucleotide triplet and the amino acid which it represents. Indeed, if such a relation exists, it would be bound to hold one of the keys to understanding the origin of life.

The general properties of the genetic code turn out to bear a curious resemblance to another symbolic system devised more than 3000 years ago for fathoming the nature of life, namely to the ancient Chinese *I Ching*, or "Book of Changes". My attention was drawn to this resemblance by John Cage, who has made extensive use of the *I Ching* in the composition of his chance music, and the detailed nature of the correspondence between the two systems was outlined for me by Harvey Bialy. The *I Ching* is based on the interaction of the two antithetical principles Yang (represented by an unbroken line —) and Yin (represented by a broken line --). Yang and Yin are combined to form four digrams, Old Yang (=), Old Yin (==), New Yang (==) and New Yin (=), and the four digrams are combined three at a time to form $4^3=64$ hexagrams. Each hexagram, which is read from bottom to top, represents one of 64 fundamental aspects of life, the nature of each aspect being given by the interaction of the three digrams of which the hexagram is composed. During the long history of the *I Ching*, the hexagrams have been arranged in several different ways, of which a so-called "natural" order was worked out during the Sung period about a thousand years ago. The manner in which life flows from aspect to aspect by mutation of Yang to Yin or of Yin to Yang can thus be understood by study of the relations implicit in the *I Ching*.

When, at the turn of the eighteenth century, Gottfried Wilhelm Leibniz was shown the *I Ching* by Jesuit missionaries, he noticed to his surprise that the linear order assigned to the hexagrams in the "natural" order is actually embodied within their symbolism. That is, Leibniz realized that Yang and Yin define a binary, or dyadic, number system, which Leibniz thought hc had only just then himself invented. Thus the first hexagram,

has the value 000000, the second,

the value 000001, the third,

the value 000010, and so on. But however surprising may be the anticipation of binary digits by the *I Ching*, the congruence between it and the genetic code is nothing short of amazing. For if Yang (the male, or light, principle) is identified with the purine bases and Yin (the female, or dark, principle) with pyrimidine bases, so that Old Yang and Yin correspond to the complementary adenine (A) and thymine (T) pair and New Yang and Yin to the complementary guanine (G) and cytosine (C) pair, each of the 64 hexagrams comes to represent one of the nucleotide triplet codons. The "natural" order of the *I Ching* can now be seen to generate an array of nucleotide triplets in which many of the generic codon relations manifest in Crick's arrangement are shown. Perhaps students of the presently still mysterious origins of the genetic code might consult the extensive commentaries on the *I Ching* to obtain some clues to the solution of their problem.

The very success of molecular genetics rendered it an academic discipline. Molecular genetics now represents an important body of knowledge, central to any understanding of life processes, which must be preserved and passed on to succeeding generations in the academies. As a subject matter for scholarly research it is far from exhausted, and indeed its technological exploitation, for instance in eugenics and euphenics, has as yet barely begun. But its appeal as an area of heroic strife is gone; all hope that paradoxes might still turn up in the study of heredity had to be abandoned long ago. And in contrast to classical genetics, which attained its academic status while still harboring the gene as a skeleton in the closet, molecular genetics seems to have no transcendent legacy. And so the world-be explorer of uncharted territory must direct his attention elsewhere. One of the most formidable unsolved domains of biology recommending itself to such romantic types is embryology. For understanding the processes responsible for the orderly development of the fertilized egg into a complex and highly differentiated multicellular organism still seems to boggle the imagination. But the recent course of embryological research suggests that it may be just more of the same old molecular genetics, albeit at a very much more complicated level. For instance, it now appears that the chromosomal DNA of the nuclei of the cells of a multicellular organism synthesizes different kinds of messenger RNA at different stages of development. And thus the specific character of the differentiated cells appears to derive from the turn-on and turn-off of different cistrons by a mechanism not unlike that of the operon proposed by Jacob and Monod. Undoubtedly regulatory circuits other than the operon, circuits which may not even exist in the heterocatalytic function of the DNA of bacteria and viruses, are also at work in developing higher organisms. But, by simple extensions of molecular genetic lore, one can already imagine what these other circuits are likely to be. Indeed, one special, and long mysterious case of cellular differentiation, that of the immune response of vertebrate animals, now seems to be nearing its solution.

Study of the immune response began with Edward Jenner's discovery of vaccination in the closing years of the eighteenth century, though by then it had been long known that persons once having recovered from the primary attack by an infectious disease are immune against further secondary attacks by that same disease. The search for an explanation of this remarkable phenomenon led to the discovery (by Emil Behring at the end of the nineteenth century) of a special class of protein molecules, the *antibodies*, in the blood serum. These antibodies were recognized to be capable of specifically combining with, and hence neutralizing, the type of virus or bacterium that had been responsible for the disease. Immunity is thus attributable to the presence of antibodies whose appearance has been elicited by the primary infection. Soon after the discovery of their connection with infectious disease, it was found that specific antibodies are formed also in response to injection into the bloodstream of nonliving materials, such as dead bacteria, bacterial toxins and snake venoms. And within another few years it was shown that introduction into the bloodstream of *any* foreign protein, or *antigen*, whether noxious or innocuous, results in a few days in the appearance of antibodies specifically directed against that and only that antigen. However, protein molecules obtained from an individual's own tissues (or from those of another individual carrying exactly the same genes, such as his identical twin) do not act as antigen in that individual. Antibody formation thus represents a phenomenon of rather wider biological significance than a mere defense reaction against infectious disease: It is a mechanism for the recognition of nonself. The capacity for antibody formation among all vertebrates at least as high on the evolutionary ladder as the bony fishes indicates the high antiquity of this process. One plausible explanation which has been advanced for the fundamental biological "purpose" of the immune response among the highest multicellular organisms is that this response furnishes a mechanism for the removal of abnormal proteins of *endogenous* origin. For instance, the immune reaction would recognize as foreign and attempt to eliminate from the body any abnormal variant cell in which a mutation in the chromosomal DNA has resulted in the synthesis of a mutant type of protein molecule. If it were not for this housekeeping function among the billions of mutable cells of a vertebrate animal, every fish, frog, bird, or mammal might well have died of cancer before it reached maturity.

By the 1930s the work of Karl Landsteiner and others had shown that a staggering diversity of specific antibody molecules —at least a million different varieties—can be synthesized by any one individual. But how does the antigen manage to give rise to the synthesis of precisely that one of the myriad of possible antibody proteins which happens to have the specific capacity to combine with it and with it alone? In answer to this question it was proposed in the early 1940s that the antigen is taken up by the specialized blood cells responsible for antibody production. In these blood cells, the freshly formed, as yet nonfunctional, antibody polypeptide chains were thought to *fold* around the antigen and thus be molded into a specific form complementary in structure to that of the antigen. This theory thus readily explained how there could exist as many different kinds of antibody molecules as there are different kinds of antigens. But this theory could *not* account for the recognition of antigens as either self or nonself, and had to be given up presently when it was shown that the blood cells which actually produce the antibody do not, in fact, contain any antigen. In any case, the notion of molding a given polypeptide chain into any one of a myriad of possible configurations ran afoul of the central dogma. For, as will be recalled, an ancillary theorem of that dogma states that the form and functional specificity of any protein molecule is determined wholly by the amino acid sequence of its polypeptide chains. Work of the academic period has now shown that antibody proteins are no exception to this theorem: Antibodies directed against different antigens do differ in their amino acid sequence, and the specific, antigen-complementary form of any antibody protein is but a direct consequence of its amino acid sequence.

In 1954, thought about the immune response received a new orientation when N. K. Jerne proposed that the role of the antigen is not to specify the structure of its affined antibody at all but rather to cause the selective stimulation in the animal of a system which was already synthesizing that antibody protein before the antigen ever appeared on the scene. The animal does not, however, contain any system capable of synthesizing antibody molecules which have any affinity for the self-proteins of that same animal. Thus the antigen is recognized either as being "foreign" by encountering "spontaneous" antibody molecules with which it can combine or as "self" by failing to encounter any spontaneous antibody molecules affined to it. Within a short time after this proposal, F. M. Burnet improved Jerne's selective theory of antibody formation by envisaging that what the antigen selectively stimulates is the proliferation of a type of blood cell whose genetic constitution allows that cell to synthesize one and only one type of antibody molecule, namely that to which the antigen happens to be affined. There must, therefore, exist in any individual animal as great a diversity of genetically different blood cells as there are antigens which can elicit an immune response in that animal. Burnet thought that this diversity is generated by mutations in the line of descent of blood cells during growth and development of the animal. This particular explanation of the source of diversity is now thought to be unlikely, and in 1967 it was proposed that the genetic diversity arises from a constant "scrambling" by crossing over of the nucleotide sequence of a few homologous DNA segments in the nuclei of the blood cells, each segment, or cistron, coding for a different antibody polypeptide chain about one hundred amino acids in length. Depending on what kind of scrambled cistron it happens to have drawn, each plasma cell synthesizes that particular type of antibody polypeptide whose amino acid sequence is coded by the scrambled permutation of its nucleotide sequence. Though definitive proof for this latest version of the selective theory has not yet been obtained and though many details are still lacking in the understanding of how the antigen manages to induce the selective proliferation of the special blood cells to whose spontaneously synthesized antibody protein it is affined, it seems unlikely that the present general view of the immune response could be very far off the mark. Furthermore, the general process of crossing over scrambling of homologous DNA cistrons and the selective proliferation of cells carrying the scrambled cistrons bids fair to be at the root also of other phenomena of cellular differentiation. It seems to me implausible that so basic a phenomenon has made its evolutionary appearance simply for the benefit of the immune response.

Another great unsolved problem of biology which still retains some romantic appeal in the face of the jejune scholarship of the academic period is that of the origin of life. Though it is not yet known, and perhaps can never be known for certain, that life did originate on our own planet (at the turn of the century Svante Arrhenius suggested contrariwise that life is the product of an "infection" of the Earth by "seeds" from outer space), the present state of knowledge of cosmology, geochemistry, and biochemistry does not put the terrestrial metamorphosis of dead into living matter beyond the conceptual pale. The continuity of modern thought about the origin of life dates from the suggestions by J. B. S. Haldane and A. I. Oparin thirty years ago that at an early stage in the evolution of the Earth there occurred a random synthesis of organic molecules in the primeval oceans. These organic molecules were then thought to form larger aggregates, capable of carrying out biochemical reactions in their own right. Darwinian natural selection then began to operate to favor the survival of those most fit aggregates which carried out the best reactions. As soon as the first self-sustaining, self-reproducing aggregate was selected in this way, life was on the scene. By the 1950s, when the composition of the atmosphere of the primitive, prelife Earth had been ascertained inferentially, biochemical experiments were being carried out in reaction vessels in which that atmosphere was re-created. These experiments showed that many essential components of living cells, in particular amino acids and nucleotides, do arise spontaneously under these conditions. But as has now become apparent, the nature of the prelife aggregates from which natural selection was supposed to pick the fittest protoorganism could not possibly have been understood before the promulgation of the central dogma. Thus we now realize that this problem actually amounts to the attempt to discover a primitive system which is capable of carrying out *both* the autocatalytic and the heterocatalytic reactions nowadays accomplished by the DNA →RNA→protein triad. That is, any evolutionary development by natural selection already demands a self-reproducing, mutable genetic system which encodes *information* for and can give expression to the characters that are being selected. There is no guarantee, of course, that the first system of this sort formed on the primitive Earth were nucleic acids and proteins. However, it seems that for the present the most promising attack on the problem of the origin of life is to probe into the origin of the genetic code and into how it could have arisen without, like Athena, having sprung full-blown from Zeus's head. Now that this problem has been clearly posed in molecular terms, it can hardly be very long until its solution is at hand. Perhaps a paradox might still be hidden here, but unless extraterrestrial life becomes available for study, it is not easy to imagine how a paradox connected with the origin of life could ever come into focus sufficiently clearly to reveal "other" physical laws.

There now seems to remain only one major frontier of biological inquiry for which reasonable molecular mechanisms still cannot be even imagined: the higher nervous system. Its fantastic attributes continue to pose as hopelessly difficult and intractably complex a problem as did the hereditary mechanism a generation ago. And the higher nervous system does, of course, present the most ancient and best-known paradoxes in the history of human thought: the relation of mind to matter. And so increasing numbers of veteran molecular geneticists are now turning toward the nervous system, in the hope that its study may soon enter a romantic phase, similar to that which attended the birth of molecular genetics. It seems likely that in the coming years students of the nervous system, rather than geneticists, will form the vanguard of biological research. One of the as yet deeply mysterious aspects of the nervous system, namely how in its development there arise the vast number of specific and genetically controlled interconnections between its constituent nerve cells, appears to be a problem on which the central dogma could be trained with some profit. But since in the establishment of that network specific recognition of one nerve cell surface by another undoubtedly plays a key role, it is not unlikely that the solution of this problem still requires a fundamentally new insight governing the structure and function of cell surfaces. Once obtained, this new insight would represent a higher order extension of the central dogma, as did the operon theory of Jacob and Monod. At a yet higher level of complexity, there remains to be understood the logic of the nerve cell network, that is to say the manner in which its circuits acquire, process, store, and emit information. To this problem there has recently been made what seems to me a quite spurious and naïve application of the central dogma. Some biochemists and psychologists have recently proposed that nervous information is also handled in the form of nucleotide or amino acid sequences. I doubt, however, that anyone really familiar either with the nervous system or with molecular genetics could see much merit in this proposal. But a few years ago there did occur an important breakthrough in the study of the logic of the nervous system. It was then discovered that relatively small ensembles of nerve cells, such as those receiving the visual stimuli from small parts of the retina of the vertebrate eye, make a yes-no analysis of the signals they receive regarding some preprogrammed question and thus send to the central brain pre-evaluated information rather than raw data. Heuristically, this discovery could mean for the study of the brain what the one gene-one enzyme theory meant for the study of the gene: In this case, the realization that no more than a dozen or so interconnected nerve cells are capable of doing in a small way what the brain does in a big way, gives hope of ultimately finding out how it *is* done.

The success which can be confidently expected for the future study of the nervous system raises an issue of some philosophical importance for our later considerations. For once the

nature of the interconnections of the human brain are sufficiently well understood, it will probably be possible to direct
specific electrical inputs into the brain. These inputs can then
be made to generate synthetically sensations, feelings, and emotions which have no causal connection to any events in the
real world. That this possibility is by no means remote was
shown by a recent experiment in which a rat was wired for
electrical stimulation of the pleasure center of its brain. The
rat continued pressing and pressing the switch sending current
to its pleasure center until it collapsed from fatigue. We can
thus anticipate the imminent realization of a further aspect of
the Golden Age, thanks to what might be called electrophys-
iological *eupsychics*. Mortal men will soon live like gods without
sorrow of heart and remote from grief, as long as their pleasure centers are properly wired.

But we may ask whether scientific study of the nervous system can *ever* resolve the mind-matter paradox. Is it, in fact,
likely that consciousness, the unique attribute of the brain that
appears to endow its ensemble of atoms with self-awareness,
will ever be explained? The principle of complementarity, Bohr
had said, would be of help in fathoming also the nature of this
problem in physical terms: "The recognition of the limitation
of mechanical ideas in atomic physics would much rather seem
suited to conciliate the apparently contrasting points of view
which mark physiology and psychology. Indeed, the necessity
of considering the interaction between the measuring instru-
ments and the object under investigation in atomic mechanics
corresponds closely to the peculiar difficulties, met with in
psychological analyses, which arise from the fact that the mental content is invariably altered when the attention is concentrated on any single feature of it . . . Indeed, from our point
of view, the feeling of the freedom of the will must be considered as a trait peculiar to conscious life, the material parallel
of which must be sought in organic functions, which permit
neither a causal mechanical description nor a physical investi-

gation sufficiently thoroughgoing for a well-defined application of the statistical law of atomic mechanics." Victor Weisskopf recently summarized Bohr's attitude in the following terms: "The awareness of personal freedom in making decisions seems a straightforward factual experience. But when we analyze the process, and follow each step in its causal connection the experience of free decision tends to disappear. . . . Bohr, an enthusiastic skier, sometimes used the following simile, which can be understood perhaps only by fellow skiers. When you try to analyze a Christiania turn in all its detailed movements, it will evanesce and become an ordinary stem turn, just as the quantum state turns into classical motion when analyzed by sharp observation." This attitude would mean nothing less than that searching for a "molecular" explanation of consciousness is a waste of time, since the physiological processes responsible for this wholly private experience will be seen to degenerate into seemingly quite ordinary, workaday reactions, no more and no less fascinating than those that occur in, say, the liver, long before the molecular level has been reached. Thus, as far as consciousness is concerned, it is possible that the quest for its physical nature is bringing us to the limits of human understanding, in that the brain may not be capable, in the last analysis, of providing an explanation of itself. Indeed, Bohr ended his 1932 lecture with the thought that "without entering into metaphysical speculations, I may perhaps add that any analysis of the very concept of an explanation would, naturally, begin and end with a renunciation as to explaining our own conscious activity." Perhaps *this* then is the paradox: There exist processes which, though they clearly obey the laws of physics, can *never* be explained.

PART II
THE RISE AND FALL OF
FAUSTIAN MAN

"If the future offered no opening to prophecy, it could not be understood when fulfilled in the present . . ."

ORTEGA Y GASSET

"Dr. Faustus in His Study," by Rembrandt. (By permission of The Bettmann Archive.)

5. THE END OF PROGRESS

In the early 1950s the beatniks suddenly made their appearance in the North Beach district of San Francisco. On first sight this phenomenon seemed to represent a revolt against the contemporary standards of middle-class America. Slovenly, sandal-shod young men and women gathered on Upper Grant Avenue to lead what appeared to be a dissolute life, in flagrant negation of the very values of the wholesome environment whence these youths had sprung. The beards and long hair of the men made them stand out from the clean-shaven, crew-cut All-American boys, though a century earlier their tonsorial habits would have made the beatniks blend in perfectly with the North Beach scene of the pioneer forty-niners. And the abnegation of lipstick and rouge set off the women from the cosmetic radiance of the All-American girls. The public attitude toward the beatniks was either an illiberal, uncomprehending hostility, or a liberal, amused tolerance, based on the understanding that revolt against parental authority and custom is a natural, and perhaps even a healthy thing. In any case, most people believed that as soon as these aberrant youths reached middle age, they would mend their ways and buckle down to the job of getting on in life. In apparent confirmation of this prognosis, the beatniks *had* disappeared from North Beach by the 1960s, at which time their former haunts came to be occupied by restaurants and gift shops catering to tourists and other solid citizens. The beatniks seemed, therefore, to have been just one more variety of Bohemians, who seem to come and go as bizarre fringe phenomena of the mainstream of social and cultural evolution.

But as its history shows, it is a mistake to dismiss Bohemianism all that lightly. In retrospect, the Bohemians of Europe and America seem to have been recruited from among the most sensitive and brightest youth of their generation. The Bohemians saw sooner and more clearly than their less perceptive contemporaries the contradictions of their surroundings and adopted radical solutions to the paradoxes of facts and mores which faced them at the threshold of their adulthood. Contrary to the simplistic view, Bohemians have generally not abandoned at all their radical attitudes and tastes upon reaching middle age and eventual reintegration into society. Instead, it usually was society which meanwhile had changed and come to assimilate what were once far-out notions. Seen from this viewpoint, Bohemians represent a vanguard whose present radical mores can serve as a prospectus for the future conventional mores of the Establishment. For instance, a retrospective look at the very first Bohemians of nineteenth-century Montmartre shows that their artistic tastes and standards of personal behavior—so *épatant* to their contemporary bourgeois—presently became accepted middle-class values of post-World War I Europe. Another example is that of the American post-World War I Bohemia of Greenwich Village. Here were then gathered young people who were repelled by the dog-eat-dog social Darwinism of American capitalism and by the venal vulgarity of its aesthetic standards. The Greenwich Village left-of-center politics and rejection of the almighty dollar as the alpha and omega of goodness were to become accepted values of the American post-World War II Establishment. The veterans of Greenwich Village did not need to conform to society upon reaching middle age; by then, society had already conformed to *their* standards. And so it would have been worthwhile to examine the philosophy of the beatniks in the 1950s if one had wanted to get a preview of what metropolitan America of the 1960s would be like.

Beat philosophy represents a rather radical departure from post-Renaissance Western attitudes, though it seems conventional from the purview of Oriental thought. It renounces both use of reason and striving for worldly success, which are felt to be irrelevant for, or even obstacles to, true living. That is, beat philosophy asserts that feelings and immediate sense experiences should take precedence over cerebration, and that realization of the self is to be sought in inner-directed rather than outer-directed exertions. By the 1960s, the beatniks had faded from view, not because they had actually disappeared but because their attitudes and styles had become a commonplace in the metropolitan areas of the East and West coasts. No one turned around any longer to take a second look at a beard or a sandal. Meanwhile, beat philosophy had moved across San Francisco Bay and matriculated in the University of California at Berkeley, though this fact had not been noticed by its then administration. It took the trauma of the Free Speech Movement to call attention to the profound change that had come about in the nature of the Berkeley student body. As the Muscatine Report of the University's Academic Senate found, an ever-increasing number of the better students no longer appeared to be "academically oriented," or "fixed upon careers and . . . seizing the opportunities offered by the University to educate themselves for a life-time of work and advancement in their fields." A group of "nonconformist" students had come to the fore, whose "most obvious feature of their outlook . . . is their outright rejection of many aspects of present-day America." These students believed that Americans "who claim to be moral are really immoral, and those who claim to be sane are truly insane . . . These ways of rejecting society in one's private life are outgrowths of the patterns of the earlier beat, or noncommitted generation." But the *really* radical aspect of the new student mentality was not the superficially obvious and by no means novel attitude of social protest but its underlying antirational basis. For "students who hold the belief that feeling is a surer guide to truth than is reason cannot readily appreciate the University's commitment to rational investigation."

I now intend to inquire into the origins of those twin aspects central to beat philosophy, the antirational and the anti-success, which had become manifest among Berkeley students.

It should be made clear at the outset that the antisuccess aspect goes far beyond opposition to meretricious strife for material reward—by the late 1950s *that* kind of success was already deflated even in nonbeat, or square society—but extends to any and all achievements in the outer world. Thus the writers of beat philosophy who set forth these notions—Kerouac, Ginsberg, Mailer, for instance—could not have been wholly beat themselves because a beat littérateur is a contradiction in terms. This same contradiction by the way, is encountered in Zen Buddhism, to which beat philosophy is strongly affined. For it is claimed by Zen masters that no person can have *really* understood Zen if he so much as attempts to write about it.

The Muscatine Report makes what I believe to be the correct identification of the source of the rise of the beat attitude among the post-World War II generation: the Affluent Society. Growing up in a society from whose ethos poverty and want have been banished, and in which a basic level of economic security is taken for granted, engenders a beat psyche to which strife for success is largely foreign. For success is a goal imbibed in a childhood spent in an *ambiance* of paramount economic want and insecurity.

I will now try to justify this portentous inference in terms of the rather old-fashioned, nineteenth-century concept of the *will to power*. This concept was central to the philosophy of Nietzsche, who considered it as the metaphysical essence of life itself. According to him, wherever there is life, there is will to power. In order to avoid such metaphysical notions, however, I shall treat the will to power simply as psychological fact; namely, I will take it for granted that in the human psyche there exists a will to have power over the events of the outer world. And following Nietzsche, I shall adopt the view that sublimation of that will to power is the psychological mainspring of all creative· activity. Undoubtedly, the will to power concept can be restated more satisfactorily in modern psychoanalytic terms, as a dynamic relation between ego and id. But I think for our present purposes it is not necessary to probe into the relative importance of conscious and subconscious components of that will. In any case, the will to power is patently one of the most important driving forces behind our outer-directed behavior. We may now define success in the broadest sense as an exercise of the will to power in which the self finds that the results which it expected from that exercise were actually met. That is, success means the ability to manipulate the events of the outside world in a satisfactory manner. These subjective findings in relation to the exercise of the will to power exert an important feedback on the self, which finds realization in terms of the success of its outer-directed behavior.

We may now inquire into the biological origin, both ontogenetic and phylogenetic, of the will to power—an inquiry that is not, of course, meaningful from Nietzsche's metaphysical standpoint. For this purpose we may envisage that the will to power has both innate, or instinctive, and received, or learned components. Its ontogenetic origin is, therefore, to be sought in an interaction between genetically determined concepts inherent in the structure of the human brain and experiential notions acquired after birth. That is to say, the will to have power over the events of the outer world does not arise automatically in infancy; instead the intensity and particular form of its development depends on ideas received from the childhood environment. And as far as its phylogenetic origin is concerned, it would follow that the will to power—a peculiarly human attribute whose appearance must have been a crucial step in the hominization process—arose through the natural selection of behavior. That is to say, according to the tautologous "survival of the fittest" slogan, natural selection favored those proto-human genes which produce a brain in which the will to power concept is innately latent. Concomitantly with this process there occurred also a selection of those proto-human groups which propagated the ideas necessary for converting the latent into the overt will to power. This argument bears some considerable affinity to Noam Chomsky's theory of the origin of liguistic capacity. For Chomsky proposes that the structure of the human brain embodies within it a "universal" grammar on the basis of which the "particular" grammars of all natural languages have been generated and thanks to the instinctive knowledge of which the child is able to master the otherwise well-nigh impossible feat of recognizing the logical structure of the word sequences spoken by the adults of his environment. From this point of view, the acquisition of language is the product of an interaction between received particular ideas and an innate general logical system. This system is attuned to these ideas precisely because they were generated by a homologous system in the first place.

Here we have touched on a special feature of human evolution. Since man passes on to his offspring not only genetic traits but also ideas, natural selection operates on him also at the paragenetic, ideational level and favors the survival of those groups which propagate the fittest ideas. [It is to be noted in this connection that the stability of the evolutionary transmission of an idea is the greater the earlier it can be transmitted in child rearing and the higher its affective content.] Thus, the early transmission to the child of the will to power of its parents is bound to have had great adaptive survival value in a generally hostile environment. The stability of this transmission is assured also by incorporating the will to power idea into the social ethos which the child imbibes, for instance, through fables such as La Fontaine's "The Grasshopper and the Ant." In having fostered the cultivation of such attributes as curiosity, ambition, and imagination, the will to power provided man with the psychological wherewithal to gain ascendancy over his fellow creatures.

Indeed, the very roots of rational thought are likely to lie in the will to have power over the events in the outer world. For the notion of interpreting the events of that world in terms of postulated causal connections must have been one of the most highly adaptive ideas in the whole of human evolution. Here, however, we may already note one self-limiting product of rational thought which can exert a negative feedback on the will to power: the idea that God's will forms part of these causal connections. That is, the greater Divine intervention in the events of the outside world and the smaller the influence of mortal will on Divine will, the less scope there is for any exercise of the will to power. I think it is possible that the gradual hegemony of this fatalistic intellectual short-circuit may have been responsible for the weakening of the will to power that appears to have taken place in such earlier theocratic civilizations as Egypt and Byzantium. That the manner of realization of basic human drives *is*, in fact, subject to evolution, and that the alleged constancy of "human nature" is a fallacy, was recognized by Nietzsche and by Herbert Spencer more than a hundred years ago. Since that time the results of comparative ethnology have amply demonstrated human adaptive processes at the paragenetic, ideational level. And, to continue belaboring the obvious, we might note that the speed with which ideational adaptation can respond to a change in selective conditions is very much greater than the possible rate of genetic adaptation. For ideas can be gained or lost and can spread through populations much more readily than can DNA nucleotide base sequences.

With the rise of civilization in the Fertile Crescent ten thousand years ago, there became possible a sublimation of the exercise of the will to power into higher spheres of creative activity, whose exclusive concern no longer had to be the problem of the next meal. In exercising the sublimated will to power, the manipulation of external events has become an end in itself. Here the self no longer finds success on the basis of mere gratification of physiological needs but evaluates whether it has managed to bring about the intended change in the outside world. Finally, this sublimation culminated in the archetype whom Oswald Spengler called *Faustian Man*. The boundless will to power of Faustian Man causes him to view himself as being locked in an endless strife with his world to overcome obstacles, conflict, to his mind, being the very essence of existence. Thus Nietzsche's metaphysic of the will to power is the philosophy of Faustian Man. Since Faustian Man reaches for the infinite, he is *never* satisfied. His personality is endowed with lifelong growth, since, never finding satisfaction in success, the Faustian self ceaselessly seeks further realization through outer-directed activities. In my further exposition, I shall adopt Oswald Spengler's characterization of Faustian Man, the epitome of the will to power, as the prime creative mover of history.

Different individuals in the same society are obviously possessed of the will to power to different extents, differences which one may attribute in large part to variations in the manner and environment of child rearing. (However, congenital, physiological variations undoubtedly also play a role in these differences.) Concerning these differences, Ortega y Gasset has said that "the most radical division that it is possible to make of humanity is that which splits it into two classes of creatures: those who make great demands of themselves, piling up difficulties and duties and those who demand nothing special of themselves, but for whom to live is to be every moment what they already are, without imposing on themselves any effort towards perfection, mere buoys that float on the waves." As individuals can differ in the intensity of their will to power, so can societies differ in the intensity and manner of distribution of that will to power among its members. And here it seems to me that a most important factor influencing that intensity is the degree to which the awareness of economic insecurity forms part of the ethos of each society. I do not yet know how to justify fully this probably Marxist view except by making the obvious point that the higher the degree of economic insecurity extant, the greater the power over external events needed by the individual for his survival. Thus the realization of this commonplace by parents and educators provides strong incentive to make the transmission of the will to power an important factor in child rearing. This attitude finds reinforcement in early childhood in exposure to the success-oriented homiletic content of epics, folklore, and fairy tales and in adolescence by encounter with the situation of the real world. It is to be noted, however, that from these considerations it does not automatically follow that in a society of general want it is the children of the poor who develop the most and the children of the rich who develop the least will to power. First, children of both rich and poor imbibe the ethos of their society and, second, some rich become, or remain rich, because of the greater than average intensity of their will to power and thus expose their own children to this quality. On the other hand, the familiar dissolute wastrel offspring of the rich can be thought to *have* arisen from a break in transmission of the will to power. In any case, the *adaptive value* of the will to power would be strongly diminished in an environment from which economic insecurity had largely disappeared.

One case of an earlier civilization in which a lessening of the will to power can be thought to have been engendered by economic causes, and of particular interest to us here because of its affinity to the beat scene, is that of the flowering of Zen Buddhism in seventh-century T'ang China. During the T'ang dynasty, China came to know a degree of internal security and economic stability previously unattained in the history of mankind. I think the emergence under these circumstances of an anti-Faustian philosophy which emphasizes the realization of self through inward-directed processes rather than through power over the outside world offers good support to the notion that economic insecurity is an important factor for the maintenance of the will to power, and hence for the perpetuation of Faustian Man. In Western society, a decline of Faustian Man set in in the nineteenth century, mainly brought about by the economic fruits of the Industrial Revolution and the social consequences of the rise of liberal democracies in Europe and America. The ever-mounting degree of security provided to the citizens of bourgeois societies then began a gradual erosion of the intensity with which the environment of child rearing engendered the will to power in the adult.

One of the first signs of this gradual change in the motivational makeup of Western man was the decline of romanticism. Early in the nineteenth century romanticism had celebrated the final apotheosis of Faustian Man in the works of Schopen-

hauer, Goethe, and Beethoven. By the latter part of the nineteenth century, the romantic notion of the self as a free agent
exerting will to power on obstacles of the outer world was giv-
ing way to inner-directed searches for the self, as reflected in
the works of Kierkegaard and Dostoevski. Concomitantly, the
Faustian ideal of the rugged individualism of laissez-faire capitalism was slowly making way for the anti-Faustian gospel of
socialism, under which the individual gains his identity mainly
from class membership and has little freedom other than play-
ing out his role in the dialectics of class struggle. But these
anti-Faustian philosophical and political notions of an intellectual
avant-garde were only the first swallows of a new spring. In any
case, their authors must have still retained a large Faustian element in their own makeup to have been able to create their
works. After World War I, the Faustian decline had become more
evident in Europe. Now talk of "decadence" and of the "decline of the West" became part of the Zeitgeist of the interwar
European intelligentsia. This general climate provided fertile
ground for Oswald Spengler's and Arnold Toynbee's views of
history in terms of an inexorable rise and fall of civilizations.
But the return to economic insecurity brought by the Great
Depression and the throwback into barbarism brought by the
rise of fascism—thus the *de facto* advent of a retrogression of
civilized life—temporarily blew away such sentiments of European *Weltschmerz*. In America, however, where despite its
higher standard of living the feeling of general economic security was much less in evidence than in Europe, there had been no
analogous widespread feeling of impending decline after World
War I. Only with the end of the Great Depression in the late
1930s did there begin in America that period of continuous prosperity which culminated in the postwar Affluent Society. The
New Deal, World War II, and advances in technology raised the
general standard of living to previously unknown heights, and
the specter of the struggle for economic survival had vanished.
Economic well-being was now taken for granted. This change in
the economic situation engendered a corresponding change in
social ethos which deflated the idea of success. And this change

in ethos, it seems patent to me, caused a massive reduction of the will to power in the first generation to be reared under its ambiance: the beat generation. A few years later, affluence following postwar reconstruction seems to have set off an analogous motivational metamorphosis also among European youth, in both capitalist West and socialist East.

And here we can perceive an internal contradiction of progress. Progress depends on the exertions of Faustian Man, whose motivational mainspring is the idea of the will to power. But when progress has proceeded far enough to provide an ambiance of economic security for Everyman, the resulting social ethos works against the transmission of the will to power during child rearing and hence aborts the development of Faustian Man. This internal contradiction thus embodies in progress an element of negative feedback. A formally analogous analysis of such an internal contradiction in progress was made by Ortega y Gasset. He recognized Faustian Man as being the mainspring of progress and believed that economic security leads to the hegemony of a non-Faustian mass man. Ortega y Gasset developed the idea that the culmination of the fantastically successful efforts of Faustian Man in the eighteenth and nineteenth centuries allowed the non-Faustian, noncreative masses to take over in the twentieth. That is, the combination of economic prosperity and of liberal notions, such as the rights of man, promulgated by earlier Faustian leaders finally gave power to the non-Faustian masses. The mobocracy of the masses, who had previously accepted their inferiority in docile obscurity, now smothered their benefactor, Faustian Man. Though I do not, of course, adopt the aristocratic frame of reference of Ortega y Gasset's argument, its net result is essentially the same as that which I am trying to make here.

Thus I reach my first general conclusion concerning progress: It is by its very nature, by its very dependence on the will to power, *self-limiting*. The secular consequences of progress diminish both the adaptive, evolutionary value of the will to power and the sociopsychological conditions necessary for its further propagation. The rise of beat philosophy has made this self-limitation so strikingly manifest in our time that it is difficult to escape the conclusion that progress will soon stop in its tracks.

On being confronted with the assertion that progress is now coming to an end, many people seem to dismiss this idea out of hand by pointing out that throughout history there have always been false prophets of limited vision who claimed that after *their* time no further progress could be possible. No doubt, these people think, there was a man in Sumer who said "now that we have invented the wheel, progress has gone about as far as it can go." Quite apart from the logical irrelevance of the failure of past for the bonity of present prophecies, it is not even true that false predictions of the end of progress are of long standing. For the very idea of progress—that history embodies a movement toward a better world—is hardly more than two hundred years old. And hence the first assertion that progress is coming to an end must be of more recent date.

As the chief historian of the idea of progress, J. B. Bury, has set forth, the idea of progress was alien to the Ancients. Their belief in the Golden Age as the beginning of history and its four ever-worse successor ages obviously represents a degenerative rather than a progressive view of history. This degenerative view caused time to be regarded as the enemy of mankind and led to the conservatism of antiquity, which admired stability and deplored change. Medieval Christian philosophy was equally incompatible with the idea of progress, since it held that until Judgment Day, the goal of man's exertions on Earth should be his salvation in another world. On Judgment Day, God will restore the Golden Age, and any do-it-yourself movement of man toward that Golden Age is rendered out of the question by his Original Sin. Nevertheless, medieval anticipation of Judgment Day did introduce one important idea unknown to the Ancients which was to provide the foundation for the later idea of progress: There is a *good* direction to history. The idea of progress still remained undiscovered during the Renaissance. For Renaissance exaltation of classical antiquity as the time when reason had reigned supreme and the arts had attained a pinnacle impossible to reascend could hardly have fostered progressive notions. But one further important element had now emerged: Self-confidence, after its eclipse in the Dark Ages, was restored to reason, and the belief gained ground that there is a purpose to human strife other than salvation beyond the grave. The rise of science in the sixteenth century—particularly the Copernican revolution—tarnished the glory that was Greece and Rome, and by the seventeenth century the first assertions appeared that modern times are actually no worse than antiquity. The French Encyclopedists of the eighteenth century discovered that the cumulative extension of knowledge brought by science causes an amelioration of the human condition and finally, upon the advent of the French Revolution, the idea of progress was given its comprehensive formulation by the Marquis de Condorcet. This idea was to become the central theme of nineteenth-century thought and found reflection in the works of such of its major figures as Karl Marx, Auguste Comte, and John Stuart Mill. In the wake of the publication of Darwin's *Origin of Species* in 1859, the idea of progress was raised to the level of a scientific religion, with Herbert Spencer as its apostle. For since the inexorable processes of evolution are constantly working to improve nature, man's condition obviously partakes in the general movement toward a better world. This optimistic view came to be so widely embraced in the industrialized nations, particularly in America, that the claim that progress could presently come to an end is now widely regarded as outlandish a notion as was in earlier times the claim that the Earth moves around the Sun.

It is now high time that I define progress more precisely. What does movement toward a "better" world really mean? Most people undoubtedly understand a better world to be one of greater *happiness*. But since it is patently impossible to make a meaningful quantitation of happiness—were the medieval serfs more or were they less happy than the denizens of present-day megalopolitan surburbia?—this definition renders belief in progress an act of faith, one not subject to verification or disproof.

So this definition is useless for any discussion of the coming end of progress. The definition of progress as "natural" Darwinian evolution toward a "fitter" human condition is equally useless in this connection, because of the tautologous nature of the fitness concept.

It seems that the most meaningful definition of progress can be made from the purview of its very mainspring, namely the will to power. That is, the "better" world is one in which man has a greater power over external events, one in which he has gained a greater dominion over nature, one in which he is economically more secure. This definition makes progress an undeniable historical fact. Furthermore, it makes possible the claim that progress will end, since the assertion that there is to be no further increase in power over external events is meaningful, even if it were untrue. This definition does not, therefore, encompass such wholly internal aspects of the human condition as happiness. Hence, it is a totally amoral view of progress, under which nuclear ballistic missiles definitely represent progress over gunpowder cannonballs, which in turn represent progress over bows and arrows.

In thus focusing on power over external events as the measure of progress, one of its most striking features becomes readily comprehensible. That feature is that progress has proceeded at an ever-accelerating rate. It is commonplace nowadays to present graphs on which diverse indices to the dominion over nature, such as world population, per capita income, speed of travel, world energy consumption, or number of working scientists, are plotted against historical time. Every such graph invariably shows a curve of upward concavity. For the first three thousand years onward from the Middle Kingdom of ancient Egypt, the curve remains practically level at a very low value, then starts a slow rise in Renaissance times, rises still more sharply after the Industrial Revolution, and shoots upward almost vertically in the twentieth century. Another way of appreciating the accelerating character of progress is to note the ever-increasing frequency of discoveries. For instance, if we consider the sources of inanimate energy discovered since fire was first exploited some fifty thousand years ago, we find that forty-five thousand years had to elapse until the next energy source, water power, was harnessed; about thirty-five hundred years after that wind power came into use; within another three hundred years steam power was discovered; the internal combustion engine followed within another century, and nuclear power became available after only forty more years. Or, if we consider the discovery of natural forces since the concept of a natural force was first formulated by the Greeks two thousand years ago, we find that about seventeen hundred years went by before gravity was discovered, followed two hundred years later by electromagnetism, which, in turn, was followed fifty years later by nuclear forces.

These dynamics of progress, and their importance for the understanding of history, were set forth some sixty years ago by Henry Adams, in his "Law of Acceleration." Adams noted that during the nineteenth century the power utilized from the world's coal output, and by inference the rate of progress, doubled every ten years. From the beginning of the fifteenth century until the end of the eighteenth century he judged the doubling period of the rate of progress to be between twenty-five and fifty years. But, Adams pointed out, establishing the actual length of the doubling period is of relatively little importance compared to admitting the fact of acceleration itself. Projecting these dynamics of progress into the future, Adams thought that to an American living in the year 2000, "the 19th century would stand on the same plane with the 4th century —equally childlike—and he would only wonder how both of them, knowing so little, and so weak in force should have done so much." In the twentieth century, however, a new social mind would be required. For "thus far, since five or ten thousand years, the mind had successfully reacted, and nothing yet proved that it would fail to react—but now it would need to jump."

Such kinetics of acceleration are well known to the natural sciences, where they are generally explained in terms of reactions involving an element of *positive* feedback: The farther the reaction has already progressed, the faster its further progress. The growth of a bacterial culture is an example of the most simple of such reactions; since each bacterium in the culture gives rise to two daughter bacteria half an hour after its own birth, the number of bacteria being born per minute is proportional to the number of bacteria that are already present, and hence the rate of growth of the culture doubles every generation. Evidently the element of positive feedback embodied by progress is that the rate at which man can gain more power over the outer world is the greater the more power is already at his disposal. Now if history is viewed as the movement of progress, then history too is accelerating with respect to calendar time.

It is just this acceleration of progress relative to calendar time (and also relative to human physiological time) which accounts for the precise moment in history when the idea of progress finally arose. Throughout antiquity, Middle Ages, and Renaissance, the rate of progress was so slow that the world from which any person departed upon his death was not very different from that into which he had entered upon his birth, even though the fortunes of his own person or community might have undergone some perceptible change. Indeed, what perceptible changes there were, were most often for the worse, such as the ravages of war and pestilence. Some progress *was* taking place during all that time, of course, but it was proceeding so slowly that within living memory things seemed to have either remained as they always had been or deteriorated. And so the hegemony of historicist pessimism in classical times, of medieval hope for redemption only after death, and of Renaissance nostalgia for the glories of Greece and Rome finds its explanation in the impossibility of any personal experience of progress in those far-away days. Toward the end of the eighteenth century, however, an "equivalence point" was finally reached. Now within one life span, the American, French, and Industrial revolutions had so obviously brought about social, political, and economic improvements in the human condition that progress had at last become a matter of personal experience. In the century and a half that has elapsed since that equivalence point, progress has continued to accelerate, so that within the memory of an octogenarian living today the world has changed beyond all recognition.

But this very aspect of *positive* feedback of progress responsible for its continuous acceleration embodies in it an element of temporal self-limitation. For since it seems *a priori* evident that there does exist *some* ultimate limit to progress, some bounds to the degree to which man can gain dominion over nature and be economically secure, it follows that this limit is being approached at an ever-faster rate. It is difficult, of course, to quantitate any limit to progress, since the degree to which mankind has gained dominion over nature cannot be expressed in terms of any single parameter. Nevertheless, if one examines one by one the parameters conceivably relevant to estimating the rate of progress, such as world population and energy consumption, per capita income, or speed of travel, one must conclude that none of them is likely ever to exceed some definite bound. And just as, according to Adams, the actual length of the doubling time of progress is of relatively little importance compared to admitting the fact of acceleration itself, so the actual magnitude of the limit to various indices of progress is of relatively little importance compared to admitting the existence of the limit itself. To appreciate this fact, we may consider a semi-logarithmic plot of Adams' Law of Acceleration. On this graph, distances on the vertical axis are proportional to the logarithm of the magnitude of an index to progress, and distances on the horizontal axis are proportional to calendar time. The curve has been drawn according to the doubling times of progress as estimated from Adams' index of world energy consumption figures. The present (A.D. 1960) level of the index has been assigned the arbitrary value of 1.0, representing a 100,000-fold increase over the (1000 B.C.) base line of 0.00001. Extrapolation of this curve into the future shows that any reasonable limit of the parameter under consideration will be reached within a period short with respect to historical time. Thus, even if the present level of 1.0 of the parameter is only one-thousandth of its ultimate limit, that limit

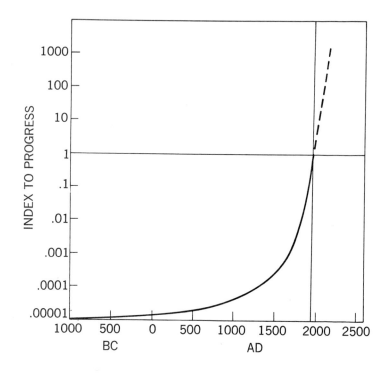

A plot of Henry Adams' Law of Acceleration of Progress.

would be reached by the year 2160. And, even if the rate of acceleration of the parameter were considerably less than that of world energy consumption, it would still follow from the fact of acceleration that any reasonable limit would be reached within a few centuries. Thus here we perceive a second general conclusion concerning progress: Though progress has occurred in the past, its accelerating kinetics preclude it from being an everlasting feature of human history in the future. Indeed, the dizzy rate at which progress is now proceeding makes it seem very likely that progress must come to a stop soon, perhaps in our lifetime, perhaps in another generation or two.

Finally we may return briefly to the phenomenon of Bohemians in general and of the beatniks in particular. First, it should have become apparent by now why Bohemianism first arose in the nineteenth century and not earlier. For it was only then that the constant acceleration of progress had reached such a pitch that important social, political, and economic changes had become not only perceptible but were occurring too fast for their general spiritual and cultural assimilation. Consequently, adjustment of mores to the secular consequences of progress could no longer occur at the requisite speed, and there developed an ever-greater discrepancy between the real world and the situation to which these mores were supposed to pertain. This lack of correspondence between the postulated and the actual human condition is most evident to the young simply because *their* psyche developed in a situation which is closer to the present than the childhood environment of their elders. Hence, the most sensitive young people, who can most readily appreciate the changes wrought by progress, become most easily alienated from the society mounted by their elders, and thus tend to emigrate to Bohemia. When the mores of that society finally catch up with the new situation, the now middle-aged ex-Bohemians no longer differ in their attitudes from anyone else; they are "rehabilitated." Meanwhile, of course, progress had caused further, as yet unassimilated changes and moral paradoxes, the appreciation of which gives rise to the next generation of young Bohemians. It is, therefore, reasonable to consider the beatniks as representing another natural link in this alienation chain, which began after the equivalence point in rate of progress and human life span was reached late in the eighteenth century. Second, we now see why beatniks represent a phenomenon of capital importance for understanding the present. It is a mistake to conclude that because of their beat attitude, the beatniks will never amount to anything, will never, unlike their Bohemian predecessors, create anything of lasting value, and will, therefore, be without significant effect on the future; here today, gone tomorrow. On the contrary, by allowing Faustian Man to make his exit from the stage of history, beat philosophy paved the way for the profound adjustments in the human psyche that are necessary if man is to bear living in the Golden Age.

The Berlin Philharmonic. Architect: Hans Scharoun. (By permission of Hans Andres Verlag, Hamburg.)

6. THE END OF THE ARTS AND SCIENCES

I have thus far adduced two, more or less independent, arguments which lead me to the belief that progress will stop in our time. One argument, psychological in kind, asserted that accession to economic security, a secular consequence of progress, will ultimately brake progress because it is inimical to the paragenetic transmission of the will to power. The appearance of the beat generation was interpreted in the light of this argument to mean that the negative feedback of progress on the will to power has by now made its effects felt on a massive scale. The other argument, kinetic in kind, pertained to the constantly accelerating rate of progress. For if, as seems *a priori* reasonable, there are *some* limits to progress, then these limits are being approached at an ever-faster speed. The rate of progress has now become so fast—such fantastic changes in the human condition have taken place within living memory—that it seems difficult to imagine any limit to progress so far beyond what has already been accomplished that this limit will not be reached soon. Of these two arguments, the second is patently the weaker, because it depends on the impressionistic finding that the present rate of progress *is*, in fact, fast with respect to the approach of its ultimate limits occurring in a human life span. I now want to adduce a third, an entirely independent argument which shows that ultimate limits are already in view in what is generally considered to be the most important indices to progress. These indices are the arts and sciences, in which sublimated will to power and exertion of Faustian Man has found its highest expression.

It is a commonplace reaction to the present situation in the arts to sense that there seems to be something drastically wrong. Such contemporary manifestations as action painting, Pop art, and chance music are causing widespread apprehension about the state of art. And this apprehension appears to exist not only among the general public but also among an important sector of the artistic community itself. (Lewis Mumford, for example, wrote recently that "the fashionable oppish and poppish forms of non-art today bear as much resemblance to . . . exuberant creativity . . . as the noise of a premeditated fart bears to a trumpet voluntary of Purcell.") Many people feel that art has somehow turned into a dead-end street and that for there to be *any* future an escape must be found from the present direction. The theme I want to develop now is that there is no such escape, inasmuch as these latter-day bizarre art forms have but followed in natural succession from the masterworks of the past. Instead of making a wrong turn, art has merely traveled down (or, rather up) a one-way street since its beginnings in the remote prehistoric past. In order to make this point, I want to draw attention to one obvious historical trend which provides the directional arrow for traffic along that one-way street: As artistic evolution unfolds, the artist is being freed more and more from strict canons governing the method of working his medium of creative expression. The end result of this evolution has been that, finally, in our time, the artist's liberation has been almost total. However, the artist's accession to near-total freedom of expression now presents very great cognitive difficulties for the appreciation of his work: The absence of recognizable canons reduces his act of creation to near-randomness for the perceiver. In other words, artistic evolution along the one-way street to freedom embodies an element of self-limitation. The greater the freedom already attained and hence the closer the approach to the random of any artistic style for the percipient, the less possible for any successor style to seem significantly different from its predecessor. I will now try to present a brief summary of what I understand to be the information-theoretical and psychological reasons underlying this dominant trend in artistic evolution. This argument is gleaned from the works of such writers as Suzanne K. Langer, Wylie Sypher, Leslie A. Fiedler, and especially Leonard B. Meyer. Furthermore, I will attempt to show later that a similar element of cognitive self-limitation is apparently involved also in the progress of the sciences, a limitation the existence of which has only recently come to light.

To begin this discussion, I will state the traditionalist assertion that both the arts and the sciences are activities that endeavor to discover and to communicate truths about the world. These endeavors became possible at that remote but most critical stage in man's psychic evolution when he turned into a semantic animal, that is, when he got hold of the powerful idea of the symbolic representation of events. The domain to which art addresses itself is the inner, subjective world of emotions. Artistic statements, therefore, pertain mainly to relations between private events of affective significance. The domain of the sciences, in contrast, is the outer, objective world of physical phenomena. Scientific statements, therefore, pertain mainly to relations between or among public events. This dichotomy of domain does not mean that for the percipient an artistic statement is necessarily devoid of objective significance (a Canaletto painting, for instance, provides information about the public event that was Venice), nor that a scientific statement is necessarily devoid of affective significance (the central dogma of molecular genetics, for instance, provided disappointment for the knights of the Paradox). In any case, from this traditionalist standpoint information and the perception of *meaning* in that information is the central content of both arts and sciences. Hence when we speak of progress in the arts and sciences we can really refer to only one thing, namely that progress is taking place as long as the sum total of meaningful artistic and scientific statements waxes. And thus progress in the arts and sciences would be reaching its end when it has become more and more difficult to continue adding to that accumulated capital of meaningful statements.

In the beginning, the origins of art were not yet art. For

example, music probably took its first roots in the organization of sounds, vocal and percussive, for rhythmatization of work and ritual and for nervous excitation. At this stage music was not yet art—no more than primitive grunts and cries were language—because music still lacked its semantic function. Only upon the gradual development of symbolic use of musical form did music become art. In the dichotomous scheme of artistic and scientific domains, music appears to be the "purest" of the arts, in that it has the least to say about the outer world and hence shows the least overlap with the sciences. The thematic content of music has very few "outer" models—bird calls, hoofbeats, and thunderstorms among them—compared to, say, the vast variety of visual impressions or prototype situations available as models for the visual or dramatic arts. Indeed, music can easily dispense with outer models, to which it could never do justice anyway. Thus the content of music is necessarily more purely affective than that of any other art form; its statements pertain almost exclusively to inner events. Musical symbolism is able to dispense with natural models, because, according to Mrs. Langer, "the forms of human feeling are much more congruent with musical forms than with the forms of language; music can *reveal* the nature of feelings with a detail and truth that language cannot approach." Hence music conveys the unspeakable; it is "incommensurable with language, and even with presentational symbols like images and gestures." "Program" music, which does attempt to represent outer events, appears to be an exception that proves the rule, in that program music is generally accorded a rather low artistic merit.

How does symbolic meaning arise from the temporal sequence of tones that we perceive? According to Meyer, "musical meaning arises when an antecedent situation [of tone sequences], requiring an estimate [by the listener] of probable modes of pattern continuation, produces uncertainty about the temporal-tonal nature of the expected consequent." This definition derives from a general consideration of the nature of information. The amount of information embodied in any event is the higher the greater the number of alternative events which the percipient expected would occur given the antecedent situation. If that situation is so highly structured that the percipient's expectation of occurrence of the event is very high, the information content of the event is low. But the *meaning* of the information provided by the event derives from the evaluation of that information in respect to past and future events. That is, for an event to have meaning, its occurrence must not only have been uncertain but it must be capable also of modifying the probabilistic appreciation of the consequences of the earlier antecedent situation. Thus as a meaningful piece of music unfolds, the listener is constantly modifying his expectations of what he will hear next on the basis of what he has already heard. His final probabilistic connection of the entire tone sequence is the musical form the listener has recognized, the structure he has perceived.

Now in the listener's process of estimating the probable modes of pattern continuation from the antecedent tone sequence, there enter not only the informational feedback evaluations which he has inferred from what he has already heard of the musical composition to which he is presently listening but also the statistical rules governing possible tone sequences which he has abstracted from his previous listening experience of other, similar compositions. And these statistical rules governing possible tone sequences are nothing other than the *style* in which the piece of music had been composed. That is, the listener can actually make an estimate of the probable modes of pattern continuation only if he has some awareness of the stylistic canon under which the composer operated. And here we reach an important point, namely that for the composition to be most meaningful, there exists for any listener an optimization of rigidity of the stylistic canon. If, on the one hand, the canon is *too rigid*, the uncertainty about the temporal-tonal sequence to come is very small and the redundancy of its information very high. Hence the listener hears mainly what he was certain to hear all along; the rate at which information is conveyed to him is very low; he has little reason to modify his probabilistic appreciation of the antecedents; he has learned very little; the piece is, therefore, nearly without any meaning. If, on the other hand, the canon is *too lax*, the uncertainty about the temporal-tonal sequence to come is very great, and the redundancy of its information very low. Hence the rate at which information is conveyed to the listener will, therefore, be very high. But the speed at which new information impinges on him may exceed his "channel capacity," that is, he will not be able to evaluate that information fast enough to abstract a probabilistic appreciation of the antecedents, particularly if the paucity of redundant information does not allow him to test the validity of his inferences. Here too the piece is, therefore, nearly without meaning. Thus for a listener to perceive a significant structure in a musical composition, it must present him with a temporal-tonal sequence which is neither too certain nor too uncertain. That is, the freedom of the style of compostion must match the musical sophistication of the listener.

From this information-theoretical purview, creativity in musical composition evidently represents the generation of meaningful new structural patterns. But here we can perceive the reasons for the historical trend for progressive relaxation of stylistic canon. The point of optimum rigidity of stylistic canon for communication of significant meaning *must* evidently move in the direction of greater freedom as listener sophistication waxes thanks to the accumulated capital of previously created significant structures. At the beginning when music consisted only of rhythmic chants, drumbeats, and vocal imitation of natural sounds, stylistic canon was at its most rigid; there existed almost no compositional freedom; listener sophistication was minimal. To create meaningful new musical patterns, it was necessary to relax the canon a little, but not too much, for instance, by allowing for the inclusion of a few unnatural tone sequences. Presently, this had two consequences: Listener sophistication rose, and the possibility to create new meaningful patterns became exhausted. A further relaxation of canon now occurred (that is, a new style was created), composition of new significant patterns became possible, and listener sophistication rose further. And so it went from antiquity through the Middle Ages, Renaissance, Baroque, Romantic, and Impressionist periods down to contemporary atonal music: the appearance of a new, somewhat less rigid style engendering a mounting listener sophistication, followed later by exhaustion of the possibilities for significant new creations in that style and resulting finally in the appearance of a new, yet freer, successor style. It might be noted here in passing that the freer of two styles is not necessarily that which operates with fewer and/or less complex rules. Obviously, a small number of very simple rules can give rise to a very rigid and highly redundant style.

It would thus follow that there has occurred an evolution of musical style from its primitive origins toward an ever-higher level of sophistication. The inference of such an evolution does not rest on any teleological view of man or music necessarily evolving toward a higher goal; it devolves merely from a recognition of the information-theoretical basis of their interaction. The kinetics of that evolution, furthermore, manifest the same constant acceleration which we have already noted to have held for progress in general. The styles of classical antiquity and Middle Ages lasted for many centuries, those of the Renaissance for a century or two, those of the Baroque period and Romanticism for many decades, those of Impressionism for a decade or two, and finally contemporary styles succeed one another within a matter of a few years. This acceleration might reflect, in part, the constantly greater number of working composers corresponding to the rise in world population. Their ever-waxing aggregate activity exhausts ever more rapidly the possibilities for significant creations within any given style, though sheer greater number alone does not, of course, guarantee a heightened rate of creativity. Thus one man, such as J. S. Bach, has probably done more to exhaust the possibilities of *his* style than the aggregate effort of all of his lesser contemporaries. And thus a more important reason for the acceleration of stylistic evolution is probably technological progress in the media of musical communication. For instance, the invention of musical notation must have been a very important first step, which finally secured the accumulation of musical capital against the vagaries of human memory. The invention of printing then allowed a wide distribution of that capital to potential performers, and finally the advent of phonograph, radio, L.P. record, and tape recorder resulted in the rapid dissemination of new compositions among a vast audience. Thus listener sophistication could rise at an ever-greater rate, allowing in turn for an ever-faster stylistic evolution.

Serial music pioneered by Arnold Schönberg represents a late but by no means final stage in this evolution. The composer has now been freed of any restraints imposed on him by the traditional dictates of melody and harmony, but his freedom is not yet total. The older canons have been replaced by the laxer rules of the twelve-tone row, but rules still do exist. However, these laxer rules have now gone so far toward reducing the redundancy of information in the temporal-tone sequence that "learning" serial music already presents a difficult perceptive problem; having previously learned one piece of serial music is of relatively little help in learning the next piece, other than the general training such learning would have provided in mastering a difficult task of musical cognition. But the final stages of this evolutionary process have now been reached with the experimental music of such composers as John Cage. For here almost all rules that would allow communication to the listener of a musical structure have been abandoned. In one type of such experimental music the temporal-tonal sequence is purposely generated by pure chance, either by the composer in writing or by the performer in reading the score, so that the form is intentionally random. In another type, the composer writes intuitively without consciously attempting to develop any particular idea or to reach any ultimate goal. Thus the listener is left to his own devices, to make of the music what he will. The structure he perceives in the piece, if any, is entirely dependent on his own personality, much as his interpretation of an inkblot in the Rorschach test also depends on his personality. Thus with this development, music as an art which endeavors to discover and communicate truths about the world *has* reached the end of the line.

What, then, do these composers of experimental music have in mind? What are they trying to do? To fathom the nature of their activity, it is necessary to appreciate that the view of the world of these latter-day artists is radically different from that traditionally associated with rational thought. This view, which Myer has called *transcendentalism*, shows strong affinities to the precepts of Zen Buddhism, in that the transcendentalist believes that concrete, particular sense experiences are the only truths to be found in the world. Any attempt to construct a reality by inferring imaginary causal relations between or among these sense experiences obscures rather than reveals the essential truth of existence, namely that every fact of the universe is unique. It becomes apparent at once that to anyone holding such a belief the very idea is anathema that the meaning of a piece of music for the listener devolves from the structure he perceives in the probabilistic connections of its temporal-tonal sequence. Instead, for a transcendentalist the music is just *there*, and any analytical cerebrations only interfere with its experience as a primary fact. Art and nature thus merge into one: there is no qualitative experiential distinction between listening to the sound of music and the noise of nature. Thus the transcendentalist composer of experimental music not only does not add to the accumulated capital of meaningful statements about the world, but nothing could be farther from his mind than intending to do so. His sole purpose is to add to the sum total of unique sense experiences of his listeners.

Our discussion of the arts has, thus far, been focused on the evolution of music, without consideration of the fate of such other important domains as painting, literature, poetry, and drama. Since this essay has already overtaxed my competence in the aesthetic realm, I shall not attempt to reproduce an equivalent information-theoretical argument to account for the historical trend toward greater freedom for artists working in other, nontonal media. But I think it is fair to say that essentially the same process of exhaustion of the possibility for creating significant meanings within a style of given rigidity adapted to the level of audience sophistication, followed by invention of a slightly less rigid style and repetition of the audience education-style exhaustion dialectic, must have been at work in the nontonal arts as well. In any case, by now nearly all of these other art forms too seem to have reached what appear to be terminal or near-terminal stages in their development formally equivalent to that of experimental music. That is, the nontonal arts have now evolved styles by means of which meaningful communication in the information-theoretical sense between artist and percipient is neither possible nor intended. As far as the visual arts are concerned, this terminal genre is represented by such styles as action painting, as practiced by painters who drip or splash paints on their canvas, and by Pop art, as exemplified by the eclectic collages of "found" objects and the facsimiles of Campbell soup cans and comic strips. As Sypher has pointed out, the unifying characteristic of these styles is the anonymity of the artist whose self finds no reflection in his works. And no more than the experimental composer does the action painter and the Pop artist fashion his works as new, meaningful statements about the world. He merely adds to the experiential repertoire of his audience, which is to make of these works what it will. Similarly evident cases of terminal stages in art seem to have been reached in drama and literature. Here, no subtle information-theoretical analysis is required to show how meaning arises from the medium of drama and literature, for the "language" of drama and literature is obviously language itself. But since playwrights and writers have not generally manipulated grammatical rules for their own purposes, drama and literature has not undergone any information-theoretical development in the use of the medium of communication comparable to that which occurred in music and the visual arts. Instead, the possibilities of using language as an artistic medium simply seem to have been used up. In drama, this exhaustion finds reflection in the theater of the absurd, particularly in the works of Eugene Ionesco. In our time, so Ionesco realized, all verbal language has become a cliché and hence is no longer suitable for communicating matters of affective significance. And so the dramatist of the absurd, like the ex-perimental composer, action painter, and Pop artist, has aban-doned the notion of conceiving his work as a message. The characters of the theater of the absurd mouth meaningless words, lack any identity, and engage in actions that are not casu-ally connected, that is, do not weave into a plot. The actor's main function is to be on stage, to be *there*. In literature, the end of the novel has become manifest with the appearance of the works of such writers as Alain Robbe-Grillet and William Bur-roughs. In their antinovels, all semblance of organization has dis-appeared. There are no rational connections between individual sentences and paragraphs, there are no characters, there is no story. Fiedler points out that the rise of the now dying novel in the nineteenth century was itself a big step toward the end of literature. From the purview of eighteenth-century epic poetry, the novel was already antiliterature, because, according to Fie-dler, "while pretending to meet formal standards of literature, it is actually engaged in smuggling into the republic of letters extra-literary satisfactions. It not merely instructs and delights and moves, but also embodies the myths of a society, serves as scrip-tures of an underground religion, and these latter functions, un-like the former ones, depend not at all on any particular form, but can be indifferently discharged by stained-glass windows, comic strips, ballads, and movies. Yet it is precisely this cultural *ambiguity* of the novel which made it for so long popular on so many levels, at the same time creating those tensions and contra-dictions by virtue of which it is presently dying."

Indeed, it is a striking fact that even in so workaday a branch of art and one so close to science as is architecture, a hint of a stylistic end has now become perceptible. For here too an element of the random in design has lately come to the fore. Nat-urally, in his efforts as an engineer, namely in designing a build-ing that does not collapse and, hopefully, serves its specified func-tion, the architect is constrained to obey many rather strict rules. But in his efforts as an artist, as a creator of aesthetic truths, it would appear that the architect's channels of significant communication are also nearing their limits. For instance, upon beholding so random a structure as Hans Scharoun's new Berlin Philharmonic, it is difficult to escape the feeling that one is beholding a work belonging to some final phase of architectural style. It is difficult to imagine any other building of a significantly different form. The Philharmonic is just *there*. The conceivable development of revolutionary new building materials or techniques, which had always brought about radical stylistic changes in the past, seems unlikely to affect this conclusion very seriously, except insofar as it might give the architect still greater freedom to proceed to the design of even more random, ultimately nonbuildings.

Possibly the cinema, being a medium of such recent invention, is one of the few art forms whose end is not yet so clearly in sight. Its possibilities do not seem to have been so fully exhausted that radically new styles are impossible to imagine. Perhaps it is for this reason that the cinema seems to have gained ascendancy over the theater in the recent past.

How, then, is the future of art to be envisaged if stylistic evolution has now reached the end of the line? Meyer is of the opinion that "the coming epoch (if, indeed we are not already in it) will be a period of *stylistic stasis*, a period characterized not by the linear, accumulative development of a single fundamental style, but by the coexistence of a multiplicity of quite different styles in a fluctuating and dynamic steady-state. . . . In music, for instance, tonal and non-tonal, [chance] and serialized techniques, electronic and improvised means will all continue to be employed. Similarly in the visual arts, current styles and movements—abstract expressionism and surrealism, representational and Op art, kinetic sculpture and magic realism, Pop and nonobjective art—will all find partisans and supporters. Though schools and techniques are less clearly defined in literature, present attitudes and tendencies—the 'objective' novel, the theater of the absurd, as well as more traditional manners and means—will, I suspect, persist." Thus Meyer envisages that in addition to those artists who work in latter-day, transcendentalist styles in which meaningful communication between artist and audience is no longer possible or intended, there will continue to be other artists who will persist in the use of the older, semantic styles. Though the former will not, of course, add to the accumulated capital of meaningful statements, the latter might continue to do so indefinitely. And Meyer says he knows of "no theoretical or practical reason why a talented, well-trained contemporary composer could not write, say, an excellent concerto grosso in the manner of the late Baroque. And though, unless he were a man of genius, the composition would surely fall far short of the work of Bach, it might easily compare favorably in interest and quality with countless works of lesser Baroque composers." According to Meyer, no such anachronistic use of past styles was made until the present time, because it was considered corrupt, contemptible, and dishonest from the purview of our cultural beliefs about originality and creation, causation and history. But, so continues Meyer, the abandonment of these beliefs and their replacement by the philosophy of transcendentalism will remove all barriers to the warming over of the styles of past epochs.

Nevertheless, it seems to me unlikely that the future use of past styles in the coming epoch of stylistic stasis will permit much further progress in the arts. From Meyer's argument it would follow that the very reason why the Baroque style came to be abandoned was that Bach had simply exhausted its creative possibilities. And, as T. S. Eliot wrote in a passage quoted by Meyer, "when a great poet has lived, certain things have been done once and for all and cannot be achieved again." Hence the talented composer of the future would seem to be ill-advised to choose the style of the late Baroque if he had anything significantly original to convey. Of course, in this case he would not be a transcendentalist anyway and might have scruples about resorting to stylistic atavism. But if the talented composer of the future *is* a transcendentalist and thus feels free to use any style, past or present, then he would not, by definition, compose in a meaningful way. That is, *his* Baroque concerto grosso would be semantically as nugatory as the Pop artist's Campbell soup can.

Whereas presentiments of a coming end to art have now become a commonplace, the possibility of an end to science is much more rarely bruited. One remembers, of course, that often-told episode of how some *fin-de-siècle* physicists thought that physics was nearing its end. The grievous error of those people in the light of the then imminent advent of quantum and relativity theories has taught later generations the lesson that one can never know what unexpected scientific discovery is just about to show up. I must admit that this hortatory tale *ought* to give anyone pause for thought who predicts an end to the sciences. But as Meyer, fully aware of *his* exposed position as the prophet of artistic stasis, points out in reference to earlier false predictions of a coming end of artistic evolution, no one believed the boy who cried "wolf" wrongly once too often, but then the wolf finally *did* come. And so even though nowadays nearly all scientists still seem to envisage an unlimited progress of our knowledge of nature, I shall now set forth some arguments from which it can be concluded that for the sciences, as for the arts, an end is in sight.

First, I want to consider briefly a possible socioeconomic limitation to science. Since the nineteenth century it has become generally recognized that the fruits of scientific research lie at the roots of economic progress and that they are responsible for man's gaining ever-greater dominion over hostile nature. Indeed, it has finally dawned on the governments of the technically advanced nations that support of scientific research has so far paid the highest rate of return of any social investment. Accordingly, an ever-increasing fraction of the gross national products of these nations has been consecrated to the sciences, which in turn have become more and more expensive to conduct. But as that quest for dominion over hostile nature is nearing its goal, as technological advances made possible by the application of the results of scientific research vanquish all threats posed to human survival by hunger, cold, and disease, further scientific research appears to have arrived at the point of ever-decreasing utility. Thus it seems possible that there could occur a waning of the present high social interest in supporting the sciences. This argument might, however, lose its validity if upon the advent of what Herman Kahn calls the "post-economic" age, the sciences are still a going concern. For by that time technological progress might have brought about a virtually infinite gross national product, a condition under which utilitarian considerations for deciding upon the magnitude of social support for various activities will have lost their relevance.

Second, and more importantly, I want to consider what I believe to be intrinsic limits to the sciences, limits to the accumulation of meaningful statements about the events of the outer world. I think everyone will readily agree that there are *some* scientific disciplines which, by reason of the phenomena to which they purport to address themselves, are *bounded*. Geography, for instance, is bounded because its goal of describing the features of the Earth is clearly limited. Even if the totality of the vast number of extant topographic and demographic details can *never* be described, it seems evident nevertheless that only a limited number of significant relations can ultimately be abstracted from these details. And, as I hope to have shown in the preceding chapters, genetics is not only bounded, but its goal of understanding the mechanism of transmission of hereditary information *has*, in fact, been all but reached. Indeed, and here I will probably part company with some who might have granted me the preceding example, even such much more broadly conceived scientific taxa as chemistry and biology are also bounded. For in the last analysis, there is immanent in their aim to understand the behavior of molecules and of "living" molecular aggregates a definite, circumscribed goal. Thus, though the total number of possible chemical molecules is very great and the variety of reactions they can undergo vast, the goal of chemistry of understanding the principles governing the behavior of such molecules is, like the goal of geography, clearly limited. As far as biology is concerned, I tried to show in Chapter 4 that there now seem to remain only three deep problems yet to be solved: the origin of life, the mechanism of cellular differentiation, and the

functional basis of the higher nervous system. I indicated my belief that the insights offered by the central dogma of molecular
genetics will presently provide the keys for solving also these
last problems. And, considering the host of biologists now standing ready to do battle and the vast armory of experimental hardware at its disposal, origin of life, differentiation, and the nervous
system cannot help but soon suffer the fate that was accorded to
heredity in these last twenty years. I do not, of course, include
the solution of the mechanism of consciousness among these san-
guine predictions, since its epistemological aspects both posit
it as *the* central philosophical problem of life and also place it
beyond the realm of scientific research.

Thus the domain of investigation of a bounded scientific discipline may well present a vast and practically inexhaustible number of events for study. But the discipline is bounded all the same
because its goal is in view. The awareness of this intellectual
horizon embodies in it a yardstick for value, since the greatness
of a scientific insight can be measured in terms of the magnitude
of the forward leap toward the attainment of that goal that it represents. Hence there is immanent in the evolution of a bounded
scientific discipline a point of diminishing returns; after the great
insights have been made and brought the discipline close to its
goal, further efforts are necessarily of ever-decreasing significance.

There is at least one scientific discipline, however, which appears to be *open-ended*, namely physics, or the science of matter. Whereas the goals of the bounded disciplines are, in the last
analysis, defined in terms of physical concepts, the goal of
physics of understanding matter must necessarily remain unde-
fined and hence hidden from view. In other words, it is difficult
to envision a set of statements that would "explain" the nature
of matter. For such an explanation can be provided only by
*meta*physics, in the true sense of that term. Thus there might be
no limit to the significant statements that physics can be expected to provide. Indeed, physics might yet generate an unlimited number of bounded subdisciplines (as, say, it generated

mechanics in the past) for the sciences of the future. But even though physics is, in principle, open-ended, it too can be expected to encounter limitations in practice. As has been pointed out by Pierre Auger, there are purely physical limits to physics because of man's own boundaries of time and energy. These limits render forever impossible research projects that involve observing events in regions of the universe more than ten or fifteen billion light-years distant, traveling very far beyond the domain of our solar system, or generating particles with kinetic energies approaching those of highly energetic cosmic rays.

Furthermore, the very open-endedness of physics seems to be bringing to it a heuristic limitation, paradoxical as this assertion may seem. Insofar as I am able to judge, the frontier disciplines at the two open ends of physics, cosmology and high-energy physics, seem to be moving rapidly toward a state in which it is becoming progressively less clear what it actually *is* that one is ultimately trying to find out. What, actually, would it *mean* if one understood the origin of the universe? And what would it mean if one had finally found the most fundamental of the fundamental particles? Thus the pursuit of an open-ended science also seems to embody a point of diminishing intellectual return. That point is reached with the realization that its goal turns out to be hidden in an endless, and ultimately tiresome succession of Chinese boxes.

For the purpose of this discussion, mathematics belongs to a special category, in that it appears to occupy a position intermediate between the arts and the sciences. Since the domain of mathematics is logic, it straddles the inner world of private events in which logic arises and the outer world of public events to which logic is applied. It is my understanding that with the appearance of Gödel's theorem some thirty-five years ago, mathematics has certainly become open-ended. For that theorem has shown the impossibility of establishing the internal logical consistency of any set of given axioms, except by making that set part of a larger axiomatic system, whose internal consistency is itself undemonstrable. It would not, therefore, surprise me to learn that mathematics too would soon reach a point of diminishing returns.

Auger considers also the possibility that there are mental limits to physics because of man's boundaries of intellect. Auger asks "whether there is not a natural limit to the range of abstraction and complexity which can be covered by human thought, and in particular mathematical thought? The number of nerve cells in the brain, though considerable, is not infinite, nor is the number of connections established between them." I find that this is an important point, even though the way Auger has phrased it might make it seem as though he has overlooked the obvious possibility that the articulation of brain and computer might provide an indefinitely large extension of the number of "nerve cells" available for thought. But there would seem to exist an intellectual limit to physics which is most unlikely to be transcended by any future recourse to auxiliary logical hardware provided by computers. This limit devolves from the circumstance that the fundamental, and I suppose innate, human epistemological concepts, such as reality and causality, arise from a dialectic between the facts of life of our infantile environment and the genetically determined wiring diagram of our brain. Evolution selected this brain (and the bent for ontogenetic development of its innate epistemology) for the capacity to deal "successfully" with superficial, everyday phenomena, but it was not selected for handling such deeper problems as the nature of matter or of cosmos. Or, stating this in a different way, our innate concepts represent an axiomatic system, which, according to Gödel's theorem, contains open-ended propositions. When we encounter such propositions and try to deal with them by tampering with our innate axioms, we pay for the gain in logical coherence with a loss of psychic meaning. For instance, though the replacement of deterministic by probabilistic causality in the consideration of subatomic phenomena has made possible their successful theoretical formulation, the results achieved seem to do violence to common sense.

Now, the obstacle to scientific progress posed by common

sense is, like the lack of imagination of the false prophets of the end of physics, the subject of another traditional homily preached in the nurseries of natural philosophy. Common sense, so it is explained to the student, told men that the Earth is flat, that the Sun moves around the Earth, and that forces cannot act at a distance. So, common sense long prevented the recognition what we now know to be true and most readily accept. In other words, yesterday's nonsense may become today's common sense. But I think that this canonical view of the obstructive role of common sense in the history of science is rather superficial since it does not reckon with the psychological consequences of this evolution. First, the present-day ideas that the Earth is round and that it moves around the Sun through the intervention of forces acting at a distance are not really developed as part of his common sense by the growing child through use of his innate epistemological axioms in dealing with the outer world of his infantile environment. Instead, these unnatural abstractions are imposed on him at an intellectually more mature age by adults. Second, it is my belief that every such act of countermanding common sense produces a quantum of alienation from reality, or engenders a partial erosion of the "reality principle" (to which I shall return in the next chapter). Thus we may perceive another internal contradiction in science: the innate axioms on which our brain bases its cognition of the outer world and from which springs common sense suffer ever-greater violation as the evolution of physical research unfolds. This intellectual process causes in turn a progressive estrangement from the reality of that outer world, loss of psychic meaning of the insights gained into its operation, and hence weakening of the intensity of interest in probing further into its phenomena.

What about the "young" social sciences? Are they not the sciences of the future, for whose development there is now the most pressing need? Surely, there remain to be discovered many fundamental principles of economics and sociology whose application will finally allow man to control not only hostile nature but also his intercourse with fellow human beings. But here we encounter the third and what, for the purposes of this discussion, I consider to be a most important obstacle to further progress in the sciences. This obstacle was, to my knowledge, first recognized by the mathematician Benoit Mandelbrot a few years ago when he began to attempt a statistical analysis of some econometric time series, such as fluctuations in cotton prices. In the course of this analysis Mandelbrot developed an epistemological argument whose applicability transcends economics and which draws attention to a rather more fundamental barrier to the easy forward march of our capacity to discover new laws in both natural and social sciences. This argument has some considerable affinity to the preceding analysis of perception of meaning in music; indeed, it might be useful for this discussion to consider science as the perception of the music of nature. The following is a rather superficial summary statement of what I understand to be Mandelbrot's general argument and his main conclusions.

Let us recall, first of all, that science—that is, the effort to abstract causal relations from observable public events of the outer world—is by its very nature a statistical endeavor. The scientist thinks he recognizes some common denominator, or structure, in an ensemble of events, infers these events to be related, and then attempts to derive a "law" explaining the cause of their relation. An event that is unique, or at least that aspect of an event which makes it unique, cannot therefore be the subject of scientific investigation. For an ensemble of unique events *has* no common denominator, and there is nothing in it to explain; such events are *random*, and the observer perceives them as noise. Now since every real event incorporates *some* element of uniqueness, every ensemble of real events contain some noise. And so the basic problem of scientific investigation is to recognize a significant structure of an ensemble of events above its inevitable background noise. This perceptual problem is thus formally analogous to recognizing the meaning of the tone sequence in non-transcendentalist music. It is, in fact, but another instance of the fundamental information-theoretical problem of distinguishing signal from noise in any kind of communcation. Hence the lower the background noise of a natural phenomenon—that is, the smaller the role of the uniqueness of its constituent events in the over-all picture—the more unambiguous is its structure. And just as listener sophistication rose in the evolution of musical styles of less and less structured temporal-tonal sequences, so did observer sophistication rise in the evolution of scientific analyses of less and less structured phenomena. Thus, most of the natural phenomena for which successful scientific theories had been worked out prior to about one hundred years ago are relatively noise-free. Such phenomena were explained in terms of *deterministic* laws, which assert that a given set of initial conditions (antecedent situation) can lead to one and only one final state (consequent). But toward the end of the nineteenth century the methods of mathematical statistics came to be trained on previously inscrutable physical phenomena involving an appreciable element of noise. This development gave rise to the appearance of *indeterministic* laws of physics, such as the kinetic theory of gases and quantum mechanics. These indeterministic laws envisage that a given set of initial conditions can lead to several alternative final states. An indeterministic law is not devoid of predictive value, however, because to each of the several alternative final states there is assigned a probability of its realization. Indeed, a deterministic law can be regarded as a limiting case of a more general indeterministic law in which the chance of the occurrence of *one* of the alternative final states approaches certainty. [Here it might be well to give a little credit to the erstwhile benighted false prophets of the end of physics; at least they seemed to have correctly sensed the end of *deterministic* physics in their time.] The conventional acid test of the validity of both deterministic and indeterministic laws is the realization of their predictions in future observations. If the predictions *are* realized, then the structure which the observer believes to have perceived in the original phenomenon can be considered to have been real.

Now Mandelbrot asserts that science is presently at the threshold of what he calls a *second stage of indeterminism*, in that many of those noisy phenomena which continue to elude successful theoretical understanding will not only be inaccessible to analysis by old-style deterministic theories, but might prove refractory also to formulation in terms of latter-day, or first-stage indeterministic theories. In making this point, Mandelbrot draws attention to the statistical character of the noise presented by the random aspect of an ensemble of natural events, or the *spontaneous activity of the system*. It is the nature of the spontaneous activity of a system which is of the utmost importance for its cognition. In almost all systems for which it *has* so far been possible to make successful first-stage indeterministic scientific theories, the spontaneous activity displays a statistical distribution such that the mean value of a series of observations converges rapidly toward a limit. That limit can be subjected to analysis of the classical deterministic type. For instance, in the successful kinetic theory of gases, the spontaneous activity of a gas satisfies this condition. Here the energy of individual molecules is subject to a very wide variation (thermal unrest), but the mean energy per molecule converges to a limit and is, therefore, for all practical purposes determined. But many of the phenomena for which it has *not* been possible to make successful scientific theories so far turn out to possess a spontaneous activity which displays quite a different distribution. For such phenomena the mean value of a series of observations converges only very slowly, or not at all, toward a limit. And here, according to Mandelbrot, it is very much more difficult to ascertain whether any structure the observer believes to have perceived is real, or merely a figment of his imagination. To illustrate this point, Mandelbrot cites the record of a century-long coin-tossing game between Peter and Paul, reproduced here. If we focus our attention on the points where the fortunes of Peter and Paul are equal (that is, where the record crosses the horizontal line), then we observe that the density distribution of those points is extremely irregular. In particular, it is apparent that the relative variability in the number of such crossings per time interval is not decreased by considering longer and longer intervals. In such a record, a wealth of detail and structure can be perceived by an interested

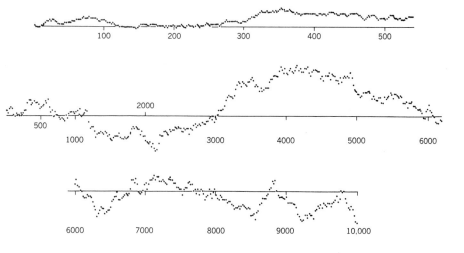

Record of Paul's winnings in a coin-tossing game, played with a fair coin. Zero crossings seem to be strongly clustered, although intervals between crossings are obviously statistically independent. To appreciate fully the extent of the apparent clustering in this figure, note that the units of time used on the second and third lines equal twenty plays. Hence the second and third lines lack detail, and each of the corresponding zero crossings is actually a cluster, or a cluster of clusters. For example, the details of the clusters around time 200 can be clearly read on the first line, which uses a unit of time equal to two plays. (From W. Feller, *An Introduction to Probability Theory and Its Applications,* second edition. John Wiley & Sons, New York [1957].)

observer (say, a gambler). But any perceived structure is evidently a mere illusion of the observer's brain that has no bearing on the random mechanism which actually generated the record and which will generate future events.

Mandelbrot suggests the Gedankenexperiment of having an explorer bring back Peter and Paul's coin-tossing record as the topographical cross section of a hitherto unknown part of the world, in which all the regions below the bold horizontal lines are under water. Evidently, this record manifests such "typical" geographical features as "oceans," "islands," "archipelagos," and "lakes." The question now is how to decide whether the formation of this topography was due to cause or to chance. Evidently, any such decision will be of the utmost difficulty. This hypothetical problem is, in fact, close to the real situation, in that the variation in the size of terrestrial islands follows the same kind of statistical distribution as does the variation in the distances between zero crossings of the coin-tossing record. This kind of distribution is called "Pareto" distribution, after the turn-of-the-century Italian economist who first observed it in the distribution of incomes. Indeed, many other geophysical, meteorological, and astrophysical phenomena, such as size of mineral deposits, annual rainfall, and energies of meteorites and cosmic rays, follow Pareto distributions. The ready perception of structure in these phenomena is, as we saw in the density distribution of zero crossings of Peter and Paul's coin-tossing game, no guarantee that they are *not* due to pure chance. And, so Mandelbrot argues, the work required to validate the reality of any structure abstracted from a system displaying the statistics of Pareto exceeds by orders of magnitude the work expended hitherto on the validation of deterministic or first-stage indeterministic laws abstracted from systems displaying statistics where mean values rapidly converge to a limit. Thus until observational efforts of truly staggering dimensions can be expended on tests of second-stage indeterministic laws abstracted from systems for which there is no convergence to a limit of mean values at all, their scientific analysis will necessarily remain ambiguous. There does, of course, exist a spectrum of intermediate situations in which there occurs a *slow* convergence of mean values to a limit, and the effort required for analysis of such systems diminishes with the rapidity of this convergence.

Mandelbrot's main point, however, pertains to the future of the social sciences, particularly to economics and sociology. He signals, first of all, that the conspicuous lack of successful theories in these fields compared to the natural sciences cannot be ascribed (as is often done) to a difference in age. On the contrary, probability theory arose in connection with problems in the social sciences more than a century before indeterministic theories made their first appearance in physics. Hence indeterministic physics is younger than economics. No, the difference seems to arise from the predominance of Pareto distributions in the basic phenomena to which the social sciences must address their quantitative analysis. In economics, for instance, firm sizes, and income and price fluctuations follow Pareto's law. In sociology, the sizes of "human agglomerations" have a similar distribution, which demonstrates that such common-sense terms as "cities," "towns," and "villages" are ambiguous, impressionistic structures. That our vocabulary contains these terms, nevertheless, is a reflection of our habit of providing a specific description of a world whose events are intuited in terms of converging mean value statistics. Or, as Meyer has expressed it, "the redundancy which we are able to discover in the world is partly a function of the organization—the redundancy—built into the nervous system." Thus, according to this argument, it may be a vain hope to expect an early efflorescence of the social sciences, because most of their laws will be of the second-stage indeterministic kind. And hence verification of these laws would often require exertions that exceed by orders of magnitude all previous efforts expended on the natural sciences. Since it is not clear at present that such efforts are within the realm of the feasible, economics and sociology may long remain the ambiguous, impressionistic disciplines that they are at present. For it may be possible only in exceptional cases to ascertain whether their fundamental laws represent reality or figments of the imagination.

It seems to me that there is a strong formal resemblance between the nugatory semantics of transcendentalist art and the ambiguous epistemology of second-stage indeterminism in science. In both cases the percipient is more or less on his own, to make of his experience what he will. For all he knows, the events he witnesses are random in their origins. Thus arts and sciences, which in remote times both began as sublimations of the will to power and, meanwhile, have been traveling along separate paths, now appear to be approaching the same condition: Much work remains to be done, but how meaningful is it all?

Better Living Thru Chemistry in the Haight-Ashbury District of San Francisco. Photographer: Edmund Shea. (By permission of Libra Artworks-American Newsrepeat Company, Berkeley.)

7. THE ROAD TO POLYNESIA

After having outlined internal contradictions and limits of progress in the preceding two chapters, it is finally time to discuss the human condition which the putatively terminal stages of progress are now likely to bring about. As I indicated at the very outset of my exposition, I envisage this condition to be that of the Golden Age described by Hesiod more than twenty-five centuries ago. For the secular consequences of progress have now readied the Earth for that golden race of mortal men who, thanks to technology, will live like gods, without sorrow of heart, remote and free from toil and grief, but with legs and arms never failing, beyond the reach of all evil. In this chapter, I shall examine the coming of the Golden Age.

Before proceeding with this discussion, however, it is only fair to point out that, by the logic of my earlier argument, no scientific reliance can be placed on my projections for the future. For in the preceding discussion of the limits to the sciences, I adopted the view that "second-stage indeterminism" is likely to obtain in the analysis of social phenomena. And hence I am obliged to admit that the causal connections which I have previously inferred to exist between the events of the past and which I suppose to have given rise to the present cannot be presumed to lead to reliable predictions of coming events. My perceptions of structure in the historical record—the Bohemian phenomenon, the antitheses of will to power and economic security, the acceleration of progress, the trend toward freedom in artistic evolution, the exhaustion of scientific possibilities—are, for all I know, figments of my imagination that have no more reality than the gambler's perception of structure in Peter

and Paul's coin-tossing record. And so one must necessarily consider my anticipation of the Golden Age an impressionistic vision rather than an objective forecast.

This, which appears on first sight to be a modest disclaimer
on my part is, in fact, the height of presumption, and illustrates
an important aspect of the present-day transcendentalist scene,
namely the deflation of expertise. For my own dilettante psy-
chologico-historicist analysis, based on a few months' reading of
popular paperback books, is thus on a par with the best work
of any professional who has devoted a lifetime of scholarship to
these same matters. After all, according to this reasoning, the
professional social scientist is no more able to demonstrate the
validity of *his* inferences than I can of mine. It is, in fact, this
deflation of expertise which made it possible that not long ago
the canvas over which chimpanzee Betsy of the Baltimore Zoo
had spread oil colors won a prize in a show of action painting.

I shall begin this chapter by summarizing a short book written about five years ago by the physicist Dennis Gabor, entitled
Inventing the Future. This book has greatly influenced my own
thinking, not so much by convincing me of the validity of its
final prognosis, but by allowing me to see the problem of the
future more clearly than I had seen it before. Undoubtedly,
other writers have made more detailed and more professional
analyses of the many topics discussed by Gabor, such as overpopulation, the future of capitalism, communism, and the underdeveloped countries, the limits of arts and sciences, and
Common and Uncommon Man. But few of these writers have
attempted the kind of global, mid-twentieth-century synthesis
of all these facets which Gabor made in *Inventing the Future.*

Gabor starts out by positing what he calls the trilemma now
facing mankind: nuclear war, overpopulation, and the Age of
Leisure. If either of the first two catastrophes is realized, mankind will be equipped to deal with it. The survivors of the
holocaust world scramble back up to regain what was lost, and
the hardiest among them would rebuild civilization. And the
effects of overpopulation, life at the brink of starvation and con-
finement to narrow slave quarters, are only too familiar aspects

from the past. But the third catastrophe, the advent of the Age of Leisure in which mechanization and automation will have rendered human labor largely superfluous, will find man's psyche unprepared, since leisure for all will be a complete novelty in human history. Boredom devolving from having no useful work to do might well lead mankind to a general nervous breakdown, similar to the psychic disturbances now not infrequent among the idle wives of the upper-middle class. Gabor writes, "in the past thirty years technology and social engineering have advanced with gigantic strides toward the Golden Age, with 'all the wonders that would be,' whose contemplation from afar was such bliss to the Victorian intellectuals, but very little has been done as yet to prepare us for it psychologically."

The gigantic strides toward the Golden Age were, of course, made only in the technologically advanced countries, while the majority of the world's population in the underdeveloped countries still lives in abject misery. But the advanced countries, particularly the United States and the Soviet Union and even, to an as yet more limited extent China, are already at work exporting their capital and technical know-how to the backward nations. And even though these exertions are not necessarily inspired by purely humanitarian motives, Gabor thinks it likely that through the inevitable ecumenical spread of technology the whole world will presently attain the same high standard of living. "Once industrialization has started," he says, "there is no stopping and no return." As far as the economics of this development are concerned, he reckons that even if the backward nations put none of their own incomes back into productive investments, an export of only 1 percent of the annual income of the "Free World" (or of 10 percent of its military expenditures) would suffice for the industrial takeoff of the backward nations. Gabor does not expect that this industrialization of the underdeveloped countries will occur within a democratic political framework, and he thinks that "if we try to impose unduly high democratic and moral standards on underdeveloped countries we shall not do them much good."

As far as the chances for nuclear war are concerned, Gabor

finds some grounds for hoping that it can be avoided, in view of both the balance of terror and the manifest political rapprochement between the United States and the Soviet Union. He is, however, apprehensive of the possibility of China's becoming a nuclear power, which, were it to happen, "would be a black day indeed for China and the rest of the world." (Gabor's discussion did not foresee, of course, that in 1968, when that black day had come and gone, the neo-imperialist policies of both the United States and the Soviet Union still remained as greater threats to world peace.) As far as overpopulation is concerned, Gabor considers the population explosion in the underdeveloped countries a tragic but temporary phenomenon. Possibly millions of Asians will die of starvation before the end of the century—as adults instead of babies, as was the case formerly. But eventually, with increased industrialization and education, the birth rate will fall to adjust itself to the lower death rate. From the long-range point of view, it is more important to pay close attention to the population density of the advanced countries, for there it will be decided whether the equilibrium density of people is to be at the Malthusian starvation level or at a level more worthy of the dignity of man. In fact, Gabor thinks that in view of the modern means of transport the Western world is *already* overpopulated. And so he concludes that the archaic joy of having large families is the one luxury that civilization cannot afford. How to persuade young couples to avail themselves of birth control and forgo this joy is thus one of the most grave questions for the future.

Supposing then, hopefully, that nuclear holocaust can be avoided and that world population will stabilize at a tolerable level, one may inquire whether or not a long-term Age of Leisure is technologically feasible. In particular, it might be asked, will there not presently occur an exhaustion of the energy and mineral resources which man is presently squandering at an ever-accelerating rate? Gabor thinks there is good reason to expect that these problems can be successfully met. Admittedly, fossil fuels such as coal and oil will not be long for this world, but once, as Gabor expects it will, nuclear fusion power has become a going concern, our energy worries will be over for a very long time. But even if fusion power cannot be realized, then other, presently uneconomic but unlimited sources of energy, such as sunlight, tides, and volcanism will surely be exploited. The foreseeable exhaustion of high-grade metal ores is likely to be a more serious problem. But here Gabor expects that extraction of presently uneconomic but plentiful ores and the replacement of metal by plastics wherever possible will, in the end, meet this challenge successfully.

So now the age-old struggle against nature to vanquish poverty is nearly over. It has been a hard fight, won thanks to man's indomitable fighting spirit and the closing of the ranks between the knights of science and technology. But because of the ever-accelerating kinetics of progress, the state of economic plenitude arrived so suddenly that human nature has had no time to make the necessary adjustments. Gabor recalls that Moses, after showing his people the Promised Land, led them around in the wilderness for forty years, so that a new generation could grow up that would be worthy of it. According to Gabor, "the instinctive wisdom of the social body" has found the twentieth-century equivalent of the biblical wilderness, in which man can wander until the new generation is on the scene which is adapted to the Leisure Age. That wisdom is none other than "Parkinson's Law" which reduces the degree of leisure that our present technology could already afford by creating enough unnecessary work and waste. The ultimate psychological, as yet mainly subconscious, reason for the adoption of Parkinson's Law was epitomized by C. E. M. Joad: "Work is the only occupation yet invented which mankind has been able to endure in any but the smallest possible doses." (Freud, by the way, did not seem to share this opinion, since he took the down-to-earth view that the great majority of people work only under the stress of necessity and that it is the natural human aversion to work which raises most of the difficult social problems.) But now that the wasteful operation of Parkinson's Law *has* been widely recognized, Gabor believes, it cannot last for very much longer. The trek through the Parkinsonian wilderness will come to an end, and vast numbers of people, particularly those in the lower intelligence spectrum, will have nothing to do. By then the new generation had better be ready for the latter-day Promised Land, where the work of a very small and highly gifted minority, or Uncommon Man keeps the majority in idle luxury. That majority, or Common Man, will be socially useless by the standards of our present-day civilization founded on the gospel of work.

Gabor now develops a series of eudaemonic propositions for meeting the threat of universal leisure. I shall not summarize them here because, in my opinion, they represent merely plans for a mid-twentieth-century intellectual's Utopia. To my mind, the major defect in these plans—education, eugenics, birth control, international solidarity—is that they ignore the motivational decay that is already in train. Gabor has by no means failed to note this trend; he makes such *aperçus* as that the ever-growing lack of hardship in the education of modern adolescents tends to make them less productive members of society, that the dedicated (and slightly mad) inventor is becoming a rarity, and that the ambitions of university students are not what they used to be. He does not, however, draw the lesson that these phenomena are but manifestations of the progressive loss of the will to power. But since the gospel of work is patently "the instinctive wisdom of a social body" that *has* the will to power, that gospel is bound to lose its charisma with the waning of the will.

In order to examine whether Joad's dictum that work is the only occupation yet invented which mankind has been able to endure in any but the smallest possible doses is really true, one must ask whether there have not, in fact, already existed affluent societies in recorded history in whose domain leisure was a prominent factor in everyday life. (Leisure *classes* that have lived on the backs of toiling masses in societies of general want are not, of course, what we want to consider here.) For if such affluent societies have existed, then their example should indicate to us how human nature can adjust itself to meet the problem posed by leisure. Gabor, despite his assertion that "leisure for all is a complete novelty in human history," is not unaware that instances of earthly paradises of leisure are, in fact, well-known. In this connection he mentions Burma, Bali, and the South Sea islands "where people worked little and were satisfied with what they had." He describes also in some detail the happy and healthy Hunzas in their fertile Himalayan haunts—he duly notes that the Hunzas have no art—and finds that "it makes one gasp with surprise that human nature *can* be like this." But, for reasons I cannot fathom, Gabor believes that leisure afforded by a natural paradise and that by a technological paradise are entirely different matters. In contrast to Gabor, I believe that leisure is leisure and find it surprising, moreover, that the obvious relevance of the history of these paradises to our present condition is so rarely pointed out.

The history of the South Sea islands, or, more specifically, of Polynesia, can, I think, serve as a paradigm for the more general evolution toward the Golden Age. These islands were settled by a hardy and enterprising race, who set out some three thousand years ago eastward in open boats from Southeast Asia across the trackless emptiness of the Pacific in search of better homes. The voyages of these men represented daring feats of navigation in comparison to which the Mediterranean Sea traffic of the Phoenicians pales into insignificance. Even the much later sea voyages of the audacious Norsemen to Iceland, Greenland, and North America appear timid enterprises in comparison. As long as there still remained some Pacific terra firma to be discovered to the east and north, population pressure on the already settled territories caused adventurous splinter groups to venture farther into the unknown, carrying with them plants and animals for the stocking of virgin islands. By early Renaissance times, colonization of the Pacific was complete, and population control through infanticide and ceremonial cannibalism had been instituted. The colonists settled down to enjoy their exceptionally auspicious environment of abundant food, balmy clime, and relative rarity of natural enemies or adversities. Romanticized accounts have undoubtedly exaggerated the degree to which South Sea *vita* was *dolce*, but the general felicity of the environment does appear to have given rise to a typical personality not too different from the popular notion of the happy-go-lucky Polynesian. Though Polynesian society was by no means egalitarian, economic security for one and all was its dominant characteristic. Sensual gratification was a matter of primary interest, while the not negligible dangers to the person presented by homicide and mayhem appear to have been faced with surprising equanimity.

For the purpose of our present considerations, it is important to note that at the time the European intruded upon this scene, a very significant differentiation could be discerned in the directions and degrees to which Polynesian sociopsychological evolution had progressed on the different islands. That is, the more distant from the equator or the more barren and rugged the territory, the greater the residual vigor, or what in present American argot would be called the "straightness" of their inhabitants. Possibly the most "straight" Polynesians were the Maoris, whose ancestors had come to New Zealand in about A.D. 1000. These settlers populated a territory which was not only much larger than any other of the islands settled by their race but was also the only one so distant from the equator that it lies squarely in the temperate zone. The Maori retained the enterprise of their ancestors, they were skilled agriculturists and artisans, they possessed strong political organizations and formal institutions of learning, and in their carving of wood and semiprecious stones, maintained one of the few vital forms of Polynesian art (the megalithic sculptures of the Marquesas and Easter Island being another of the few instances of vital Polynesian art). The foremost factor in Maori life, however, was war, which constituted its chief business and ideological mainspring.

On the other end of the social spectrum from New Zealand were the Society Islands, in particular Tahiti. These islands, where nature was at its most felicitous and vegetation at its lushest, were settled at about the time of Christ. And here an evolution set in which resulted in what we would now recognize as a beat society. In this hedonistic culture, neither religion nor art, nor any kind of intellectual activity flourished. The Tangaroa monotheism of the enterprising settler-navigators had degenerated into a formless pantheism, there was no laborious sculpture of colossal stone statuary, and the art of pottery and the use of ideographic writing were lost. And precisely that aspect of Polynesia, and of Tahiti in particular, which has inspired so much of the romanticization since its discovery by Europeans is also of interest for us here because of the obvious analogous evolution in our affluent society: its sexual mores. Evidently the repression of the sexual drive, a nearly ubiquitous and supposedly very ancient aspect of human nature, suffered an extensive derepression in the paradise of the South Seas. Sexual promiscuity among adolescents was the general rule, and though the custom of marriage among adults was still retained, the structure of the resulting family became very loose. Serial polygamy —easy and frequent divorces and remarriages—obtained, and though adultery remained formally proscribed, its occurrence was very common. The sexual license of Tahiti found its apotheosis in the Arioi Society. This society, which appears to have arisen as a magico-religious sect in earlier days, developed into an organization of traveling performers of what by European standards were highly obscene rites. The male and female *sociétaires* possessed each other in common, and society rules demanded that all offspring resulting from their unions were to be killed at birth. Another aspect of Polynesian life highly relevant to our affluent society is the important role played by kava, a psychedelic drug extracted from the root of the plant *Piper methysticum*. In its use of kava, as in its sexual practices, Tahiti seems to have shown an extreme development. Whereas at the time of the first European visits kava drinking was confined mainly to highly ritualized ceremonial occasions in western Polynesia, in Tahiti kava was in free use for frequent, personal hallucinatory trips.

Quite apart from any restrictions imposed on historical interpretation by "second-stage indeterminism," it is in any case obviously dangerous to prophesy the future on the basis of historical precedent. However similar some earlier situation might
appear to the present, one seemingly trivial difference between
then and now, there and here, might, in fact, be of such great
importance for our destiny that it could easily vitiate the predictive value of any comparison. And thus one must be careful
not to overstrain the analogy between Polynesia and the coming
Golden Age, in which technology will soon provide for Everyman what a felicitous constellation of natural circumstances
once provided for the South Sea islanders. But, if nothing else,
the history of Polynesia does show that the "threat" of leisure
was met at least once before by simply and easily abandoning
the gospel of work. It shows that people will not neccessarily
go stark, raving mad when, in a background of economic security, most of them no longer have much useful employment.
Furthermore, that history lends additional support to the notion
I tried to develop earlier that economic insecurity is a necessary
condition for the paragenetic transmission of the will to power,
and *a fortiori* for the perpetuation of the pinnacle of its sublimation: Faustian Man. The Vikings of the Pacific must have
started out on their eastward trek with a strong Faustian bent,
but by the time Captain Cook found them, Faustian Man had all
but disappeared from the Society Islands.

The Polynesian example now allows us to perceive that even
though, as Gabor says, in the past thirty years technology and
social engineering have advanced with gigantic strides toward
the Golden Age, it is *not* true that very little has yet been done
to prepare us for it psychologically. On the contrary, the rise
of beat philosophy engendered by negative feedback of the accession to economic security in the affluent society on the will
to power is precisely such a preparation. Obviously, the prospect of universal leisure holds little terror for beat society.

But though the beat, or Polynesian answer to the leisure
problem posed by the Golden Age is certainly one feasible so-

lution, it might not necessarily follow that it is the only one. Gabor, for instance, puts his hope in the appearance of what he calls "Mozartian Man," a hypothetical creative type of which he believes Mozart to be a premature forerunner, "whose art does not live on conflict but who creates for joy, out of joy." Mozartian Man will make the most of the creative opportunities provided by the leisure afforded him and thus furnish inspiration for his less gifted and mainly unemployed fellow men, who, through appropriate education, he keeps from drink and crime. A similar optimistic view of the Golden Age has been developed by another physicist, John Platt, in his book *The Step to Man*. Unlike Gabor, who *is* worried but hopeful, Platt is positively elated by the prospect of universal leisure. He envisages that man will at last be liberated from the shackles of menial toil and can now proceed to consecrate his boundless energy, hitherto largely wasted on base activities, entirely to higher, creative things. But as I have tried to show, the "creative" activity of Gabor's Mozartian Man, or of Platt's equivalent, will, in any case, be of a qualitatively different nature from what, I daresay, these authors had in mind. In the arts, our future Mozart is most unlikely to bear any resemblance to his namesake. He will be either a transcendentalist whose creations are not intended to convey any meaning, particularly not joy, or an epigone working in one of the traditionally semantic styles which had seen its heyday long ago. In the sciences, our future genius will be similarly engaged in activities whose significance would be unlikely to make a deep impression on Gabor or Platt. He might be working out the detailed genetic map of yet one more species of bacteria or searching for one more class of subatomic particle. Or he might be a social scientist who is developing yet one more subjective interpretation of data whose statistical nature puts them beyond the pale of successful theoretical formulation. He might even be collecting rock samples on Mars, in which case we could ask him, as Arthur Koestler wanted to ask Space Cadet Tom Corbett (in a quotation cited by Gabor): "Was your journey really necessary?"

It must be obvious that beat philosophy and transcendentalism are closely affined, even though I had previously discussed them within somewhat different contexts. Evidently, the inner-directed, antirational attitude of the beatnik renders him the natural audience for the meaningless works of transcendentalist art. Beat philosophy, furthermore, seems to be exactly the suitable psychic infrastructure for the scientist of the future, in view of the previous inference that the sciences are rapidly approaching the limits of their significant progress. The beat scientist would derive his satisfaction from the experience of merely being in his laboratory and doing experiments that are meaningful to *him*. Whether the results he obtains are really original, correct, or of significance for anyone else is of small concern. In this way, science can go on and on, though, like art, it will bear only a superficial resemblance to what had been understood by that term in the past. Indeed, in addition to meeting the threat of universal leisure, the rise of beat philosophy will get mankind off another horn of Gabor's trilemma: nuclear war. As far as I can see, a beat society provides a much more durable guarantee against atomic holocaust than the balance of terror. Presently no one will be any longer *interested* in such outer-directed expressions of the will to power as the making of war. In any case, ideology and economics, traditionally the two principal causes for war, will have lost most of their relevance for the transcendentalists of the Golden Age.

Finally, I want to consider the most recent Bohemian phenomenon, namely the hippies, whose appearance in the Haight-Ashbury district of San Francisco in 1966 signaled a further adaptive step toward the Golden Age. I first became aware of this fact when I saw Lucas Cranach's painting "The Golden Age" (which appears as the frontispiece of this book) on a visit to the Munich Pinakothek Museum. It suddenly dawned on me that the subject of Cranach's four-hundred-year-old painting was nothing other than a prophetic vision of a hippie be-in in San Francisco's Golden Gate Park. The hippies are evidently a successor phenomenon to the beatniks, from whom they have taken over the inner-directed, antirational, existential attitude. However, the hippies have thrown over-board some more pieces of the traditional motivational baggage and retain but the tiniest residue of the once mighty will to power. With the appearance of the hippies there has become manifest a metamorphosis of the traditional human psyche even more radical than the resignation of the will to power, namely an erosion of what Freud called the *reality principle*. According to Freud, for some time after birth the child's self includes the sum total of its experiences, of both internal and external prov-enance. Only at later stages of its development does the child come to distinguish between these two experiential sources. It restricts the self to the world of internal events and begins to construct an external reality on the basis of the emanations from the world of outside events. The capacity to make this distinc-tion is, it goes without saying, of the utmost survival value, and its failure is, according to Freud, the cause of important psychotic syndromes. Needless to say, possession of the reality principle is a precondition for possession of the will to power, through which the self seeks hegemony over events in the out-side world. Freud outlined several, not necessarily mutually ex-clusive, avenues toward a deflation of the reality principle. One of these is represented by a reduced shrinkage of the infantile, all-inclusive self. In such persons, the adult self still encom-passes many of the events of the outside world, a condition which Freud referred to as an "oceanic feeling," a feeling of oneness with the universe. Another way of deflating the reality principle is the willful reduction of the import of outside events, either by the use of drugs or by the control of the instincts, as in the practice of Yoga. It is of no little significance that both of these assaults on the reality principle form important parts of the teaching of Oriental philosophies that are now finding ever-greater resonance in the West. In some sense, the reality princi-ple suffered premature erosion in the East. For the economic productivity of those societies had reached a level high enough for only a tiny fraction of the people to embrace views so clearly detrimental for survival in a *de facto* hostile nature. Indeed, it may well be that widespread, *partial* adoption of these philosophies to the degree still compatible with physical survival in such countries as India and China led to the later stagnation of these formerly dynamic civilizations. But in the leisure society of the Golden Age, adhesion to the reality principle will no longer be so critical for survival.

Although the beatniks had greatly deflated their will to power and thus resigned much of the ambition to change the outer world, they nevertheless still seemed to maintain considerable contact with reality. Thus the sense experiences from which the inner-directed realization of the self was sought were in the main of external provenance, as testified to by the interest of the beatniks in such activities as travel, food and drink, jazz, poetry, and sex. The use of hallucinatory drugs, though not foreign to the beatniks, did not assume nearly the importance that it was to reach on the hippie scene a decade later. Now, however, the much more extensive use of drugs as an experiential source has brought about a rather far-reaching abnegation of reality, or as its prophet of psychedelia, Timothy Leary, calls it, "dropping out." That is, the boundary between the real and the imagined has been dissolved. For the hippies, the reality principle is all but dead. This overt erosion of the reality principle embodied in the hippies was not, of course, invented in the Haight-Ashbury district. On the contrary, the philosophical basis of reality has been the subject of critical discussions for some two hundred years, ever since Immanuel Kant claimed that, in the last analysis, the real world is a subjective concept rather than an objective fact. The transcendentalist world picture of the present avant garde artists, mentioned in the preceding chapter, is evidently another latter-day reflection of this trend to lessen the importance of distinguishing between the real and the imagined. The lessening of this distinction appears also to be the theme of such latter-day films as Resnais' *Last Year at Marienbad* and Antonioni's *Blow-Up*. But the novelty of the hippies consists in their being the first large-scale community in the West which actually *acts* according to these ideas.

Finally, I will attempt to synthesize my preceding considerations into an image of the coming Golden Age. This synthesis must obviously assume that there will be no nuclear war, an assumption which is based mainly on optimism. But failure of that assumption would render all present considerations of man's future nugatory in any case. If nuclear war can be avoided in the *near* future, then I believe that the general waning of the will to power will presently lead to a condition in which the holocaust will become increasingly less probable, because interest in war will be largely gone. Following Gabor's projections, I believe that the presently underdeveloped nations will, sooner or later, reach the same level of economic affluence as that presently enjoyed by the technologically advanced nations. These economic changes will, in turn, engender the global hegemony of beat attitudes, which, in the Orient, at least, are already deeply rooted in philosophical tradition. I also assume that there will be no technological or biological developments as radical as the achievement of travel faster than the speed of light or the enlargement and structural alteration of the human brain. Failure of this latter assumption would set off an entirely new phase in human evolution, whose course cannot be envisaged by simple extension of past history.

With these assumptions one arrives at the conclusion that the Golden Age will not be very different from a re-creation of Polynesia on a global scale. (It is not unreasonable to expect that the high rate of infanticide and homicide of old-time Polynesia will not be a feature of the Golden Age, since more humane means of avoiding overpopulation are now available.) Though there will never be enough Tahitis to accommodate the world's population, comfortably air-conditioned metropolitan apartments will easily provide a satisfactory ersatz for authentic beachcombing. The will to power will not have vanished entirely, but the distribution of its intensity among individuals will have been drastically altered. At one end of this distribution will be a minority of the people whose work will keep intact the technology that sustains the multitude at a high stand-

ard of living. In the middle of the distribution will be found
a type, largely unemployed, for whom the distinction between
the real and the illusory will still be meaningful and whose
prototype is the beatnik. He will retain an interest in the world
and seek satisfaction from sensual pleasures. At the other end
of the spectrum will be a type largely unemployable, for whom
the boundary of the real and the imagined will have been
largely dissolved, at least to the extent compatible with his physical survival. His prototype is the hippie. His interest in the
world will be rather small, and he will derive his satisfaction
mainly from drugs or, once this has become technologically
practicable, from direct electrical inputs into his nervous system. This spectral distribution, it will be noted, bears some considerable resemblance to the Alphas, Betas, and Gammas in
Aldous Huxley's *Brave New World*. However, unlike Huxley,
I do not envisage this distribution to be the result of any purposive or planned breeding program, but merely a natural population heterogeneity engendered mainly by differences in childhood
history. Furthermore, in contrast to the low-grade producer
roles assigned to Betas and Gammas, beatniks and hippies will
play no socioeconomic role other than being consumers.

As far as culture is concerned, the Golden Age will be a
period of general stasis, not unlike that envisaged by Meyer for
the arts. Progress will have greatly decelerated, even though
activities formally analogous to the arts and sciences will continue. It is obvious that Faustian Man of the Iron Age would
view with some considerable distaste this prospect of his affluent
successors, devoting their abundance of leisure time to sensual
pleasures, or what is even more repugnant to him, deriving private synthetic happiness from hallucinatory drugs. But Faustian
Man had better face up to the fact that it is precisely *this*
Golden Age which is the natural fruit of all his frantic efforts,
and that it does no good now to wish it otherwise. Millennia of
doing arts and sciences will finally transform the tragicomedy
of life into a happening.

BIBLIOGRAPHY

PROLOGUE

Hesiod, The Works and Days

1. THE CLASSIC PERIOD

L. C. Dunn, ed., *Genetics in the 20th Century. Essays on the Progress of Genetics during Its First 50 Years.* Macmillan, New York (1951).

A. H. Sturtevant, *A History of Genetics.* Harper & Row, New York (1965).

2. THE ROMANTIC PERIOD

N. Bohr, "Light and Life," *Nature 131*, 421, 457 (1933). An extensive discussion of these ideas of Bohr's, and of their later misinterpretations and misuses to resurrect vitalism, can be found in Chapter 8 of P. Frank, *Modern Science and Its Philosophy*, Harvard University Press (1949).

J. Cairns, G. S. Stent, and J. D. Watson, eds., *Phage and the Origins of Molecular Biology.* Cold Spring Harbor Laboratory of Quantitative Biology, Cold Spring Harbor, New York (1966).

M. Delbrück, "A Physicist Looks at Biology," *Transactions Connecticut Academy of Arts and Sciences 38*, 173 (1949). (Reprinted in *Phage and the Origins of Molecular Biology*.)

T. S. Kuhn, *The Structure of Scientific Revolutions.* University of Chicago Press, Chicago (1962).

E. Schrödinger, *What is Life?* Cambridge University Press, New York (1945).

3. THE DOGMATIC PERIOD

4. THE ACADEMIC PERIOD

M. F. Perutz, *Proteins and Nucleic Acids: Structure and Function.* Elsevier, Amsterdam (1962).

G. S. Stent, *Molecular Biology of Bacterial Viruses.* Freeman, San Francisco (1963).

J. D. Watson, *Molecular Biology of the Gene.* Benjamin, New York (1965).

———, *The Double Helix.* Atheneum, New York (1968).

D. E. Wooldridge, *The Machinery of the Brain*. McGraw-Hill, New York (1963).

5. THE END OF PROGRESS

Henry Adams, *The Education of Henry Adams*, Chapters 23 and 24. Massachusetts Historical Society, Boston (1918).

H. D. Aiken, *The Age of Ideology: The 19th Century Philosophers*. Mentor Books, New York (1956).

J. B. Bury, *The Idea of Progress*. MacMillan, New York (1932); reprint, Dover Publications, New York (1955).

J. Ortega y Gasset, *The Revolt of the Masses*. Mentor Books, New York (1950).

C. Muscatine, chm., *Education at Berkeley, Report of the Select Committee on Education*. University of California, Berkeley (1966).

A. Parry, *Garrets and Pretenders. A History of Bohemianism in America*. Dover Publications, New York (1960).

6. THE END OF THE ARTS AND SCIENCES

L. A. Fiedler, *Waiting for the End*. Delta Books, New York (1964).

Susanne K. Langer. *Philosophy in a New Key*. Mentor Books, New York (1948).

B. Mandelbrot, New Methods in Statistical Economics. *Journal of Political Economy* 71, 421 (1963).

L. B. Meyer, *Music, the Arts and Ideas*. University of Chicago Press, Chicago (1967).

D. J. de Solla Price, *Science Since Babylon*. Yale University Press, New Haven (1962).

7. THE ROAD TO POLYNESIA

P. H. Buck, *Vikings of the Pacific*. University of Chicago Press, Chicago (1959).

D. Gabor, *Inventing the Future*. Penguin Books, Harmondsworth, England (1964).

R. L. Heilbronner, *The Future as History*. Grove Press, New York (1961).

A. Huxley, *Brave New World Revisited*. Perennial Library, New York (1965).

J. R. Platt, *The Step to Man*. Wiley, New York (1966).

R. C. Suggs, *The Island Civilizations of Polynesia*. Mentor Books, New York (1960).

R. W. Williamson and R. Piddington, *Essays in Polynesian Ethnology*, Cambridge University Press (1939).

INDEX